Volume 6 of the American Wildlife Region Series

# WILDLIFE OF THE NORTHERN

# ROCKY MOUNTAINS

Including common Wild Animals and Plants

By William H. Baker, PhD.
Head, Department of Biological Sciences
University of Idaho, Moscow, Idaho

Earl J. Larrison, M. S.
Associate Professor of Zoology
University of Idaho, Moscow, Idaho

Charles Yocom, PhD.
Professor and Coordinator of Game Management
Humboldt State College, Arcata, California

and

Iain J. W. Baxter, B. S.
Calgary, Alberta

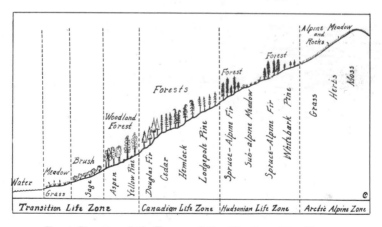

Chart Showing Life Zones of the Northern Rockies

Published by Naturegraph Publishers, Inc., Happy Camp, California

Paper Edition    ISBN 0-911010-10-6
Cloth Edition    ISBN 0-911010-11-4

The map on this page shows the principal areas covered by the Northern Rocky Mountains Wildlife Region. Many smaller mountain ranges in the same general area contain similar forms of life.

# INTRODUCTION

This book is the sixth of a series on the wildlife regions of America. Wildlife regions, such as the Northern Rocky Mountain Wildlife Region, are distinctive natural geographic areas of similar climate and topography, which tend to have characteristic plants and animals within their boundaries. Rigid lines of separation cannot be drawn because of the overlapping transitional areas between regions. Some species appear in two or more regions.

The Northern Rocky Mountain Region, as defined here, includes the high mountains, plateaus and foothills of the northern portion of the Rockies. It extends from northeastern Oregon and northeastern Washington through much of Idaho, Montana, Wyoming and northern Utah, then north through eastern British Columbia and western Alberta in Canada. It is bounded on the east by the northern Great Plains Region, on the south by the Great Basin Wildlife Region and the Southern Rocky Mountain Wildlife Region, and on the west by the Palouse Region. Extensions of the Northern Rocky Mountain Wildlife Region appear in the midst of other regions as mountain islands covered with typical indicator plants. Examples of such areas are the Blue and Wallowa Mountains, Okanogan Highlands, Steens Mountains, the Bighorn Mountains, Wasatch Mountains and the Black Hills of South Dakota.

There are four Life Zones present in this region if we use the well-known and popular system which was originally described by C. Hart Merriam for the Rocky Mountain Region. Each of these and its principal habitats are listed in the Table of Contents and are diagrammed in a chart on page 1.

In the first part of this book the plants are grouped by vegetational communities or **habitats.** Photographs of these plant communities are shown at the beginning of each section along with a short account. Following the descriptions of the plants of each habitat is a list of other common plants likely to be observed in that habitat. Learning to recognize these habitats will be of great help in later learning to identify the common animals found in each.

In later parts of this book the mammals, birds, reptiles and amphibians likely to be seen in this region are illustrated and described. In order to simplify these descriptions the area discussed in this book is described as "our region". When you are passing through a particular habitat, you will need to carefully study the list and descriptions of the animals and plants that may be found in these surroundings.

## ABBREVIATIONS

T = Transition Zone, C = Canadian Zone, H = Hudsonian Zone, A = Arctic-Alpine Zone. * * * ♂ = male; ♀ = female.

Alp. = artic-alpine meadows and rocklands; Asp. Wdl. = aspen woodland; Conif. = main coniferous forests; Grass = grasslands; Intr. = introduced; Jun. Mah. = juniper-mountain mahogany woodland; Marsh = marshes, bogs, swamps; Mead. = mountain streamsides and meadows; Rocks = rocky slides and cliffs; Sage = sagebrush; Str. Wd. = streamside woodland; Sub-Alp. = sub-alpine forest and meadows; Water = streams, ponds, lakes.

# KEY TO PLANT PARTS

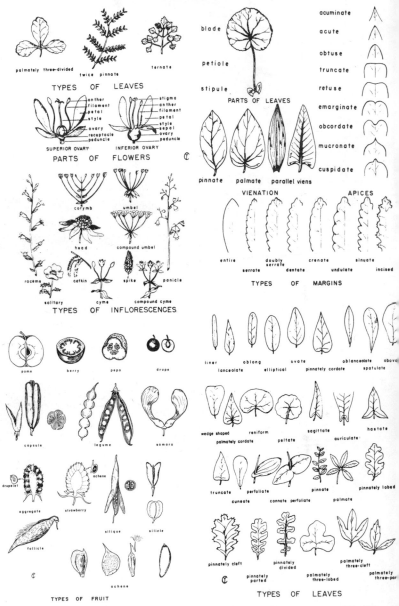

As you study plants in the field or those you have collected, note how the parts compare with those illustrated on this page. Also turn to this page when you find a plant part, given in a description, which you do not know. Practice in this sort of comparison will greatly help in the identification of common plants in the field.

## COMMON PLANTS AND WILDLIFE HABITATS

Only the common plants of the northern Rockies are included in this book. Often the selection of a given plant is quite arbitrary. A complete list of all the plants occurring in the Northern Rocky Mountains would fill a very large book. Illustrations and short descriptions along with habitat and distribution of each plant are given in the text. It will aid in understanding the descriptions if the illustrations of the plant parts and parts of a grass are carefully studied. Most plants described are what are called typical or indicator species for the various habitats listed, and so are very useful in determining what habitat or plant communitiy you are hiking in or visiting at any one time. Use this knowledge to help you identify the common animals of each habitat, as shown by the habitat abbreviations shown beside each species description. All plants are numbered and these numbers are useful in locating species when such species are listed separate from their descriptions. No mention is made of range if the species is found in most of the region. All edible plants are marked with an * in front of name.

Photo by Charles Yocom. Typical pond of mountains.

### FRESH WATER, MARSHES, LAKES, STREAMS

This habitat can be divided into two parts, Water (including lakes, ponds and streams) and Marsh, since some animals prefer marsh lands to live in rather than fresh water areas. The plants living in water usually are classified as submerged aquatics, and free floating aquatics. Marsh plants, more often, are rooted plants with floating leaves or emergent water plants growing in shallow water or wet sands. Some of the shrubs described here are found on wet shores and may or may not grow in the water.

1. COMMON CAT-TAIL (Typha latifolia). Stems stout, 3-6' high; leaves flat, long tapering, 1/2-1" wide, sheathing at the base; upper part of spike is staminate, lower portion pistillate, dark brown to nearly black and fuzzy, the   T
Water
Marsh

two parts usually contiguous (in contact or almost so); pollen grains in 4's.

**T**
**Water**
**Marsh**

*2. NARROW-LEAVED CAT-TAIL (Typha angustifolia). Stems slender, 3-9' tall; leaves narrowly linear. 1/4-1/2" wide, strongly convex on the back, dark green, the staminate part of the spike usually separated from the light brown pistillate portion; pollen grain single. Widely distributed.

**T**
**Water**
**Marsh**

3. COMMON WATER-PLANTAIN (Alisma plantago-aquatica). Stem 1-3' tall; leaves all basal, ovate to oblong or elliptic, acute at the tip, almost heart-shaped or rounded at the base; flowers white, borne on long pedicels in panicles of 3-6 branches in a whorl; achenes approximately 10, arranged in a circle around the receptacle. Margins of ponds, streams.

**T**
**Water**
**Marsh**

*4. ARROW-HEAD (Sagittaria cuneata). Stems 2-18" tall, about as long as the basal arrow-shaped leaves; the basal lobes of the leaves little divergent (only slightly away from parallel); flowers white in whorls of 3; flowers with stamens borne above the pistillate flowers on the stems; rarely only one sex present on a plant; achenes (fruits) broadly winged all around; beak minute, erect. Shallow ponds, lakes and slow streams.

**T**
**Water**

*5. WILD RICE (Zizania aquatica). Tall robust aquatic annual with stems 3-6' tall, often decumbent (lying on ground but with end of stem rising) at the base and rooting at the nodes (stem joints); leaf sheaths hairless, somewhat inflated, blades elongate, 1/2-2" wide, flat, densely hairy at the base on both surfaces; panicle large, 1-2' long, terminal (at end of stem); upper branches erect, bearing appressed (lying flat) pistillate spikelets, tardily deciduous; the lower branches bearing pendulous staminate spikelets, early deciduous; spikelets 1-flowered; lumes (bracts at base of spikelet) obsolete (indistinct or absent). Usually found in shallow water; mainly in Idaho in our region. An important waterfowl food plant.

**T**
**Marsh**
**Meadow**
**Grass**
**Asp. Wdl.**
**Str. Wd.**

*6. COMMON CAMAS (Camassia quamash). Stem slender, 6-24" tall, arising from a coated edible bulb; leaves numerous, grass-like; flowers dark blue to whitish, borne in a loose raceme; fruit an oblong capsule.

**CH**
**Marsh**
**Str. Wd.**
**Meadow**
**Sub-Alp.**

7. BOG BIRCH (Betula glandulosa). Small branching shrub, 1-6' tall; leaves roundish, very firm, crenately-toothed, glabrous (without hair), rounded at tip, wedge-shaped at base, dark green above, paler beneath, dotted with glands; staminate catkins solitary, 1" long, pistillate catkins smaller, lobes of scales about equal, wings of nutlet thin, narrower than the body. Bogs, lake-shores, streambanks and meadows.

**TC**
**Water**
**Marsh**

8. YELLOW POND LILY (Nuphar polysepalum). Leaves 6-12" wide and 7-15" long, rounded at the apex, deeply heart-shaped, floating, borne on long petioles; flowers yellow, solitary on long peduncles; stamens numerous with red anthers and yellow filaments; fruit ovoid, leathery, berry-like, 1-2" wide; seeds large, yellowish, numerous.

**HA**
**Marsh**
**Meadow**

9. HEART-LEAVED MARSH-MARIGOLD (Caltha leptosepala). Stem 2-12" tall, glabrous, thick; leaves all basal, roundish-ovate, longer than broad, heart-shaped at the base, lobes open, margins entire or shallowly-toothed; flowers mostly solitary or 2, white, faintly bluish below; fruit a slightly spreading follicle, about 1/2" long. Marshes and meadows.

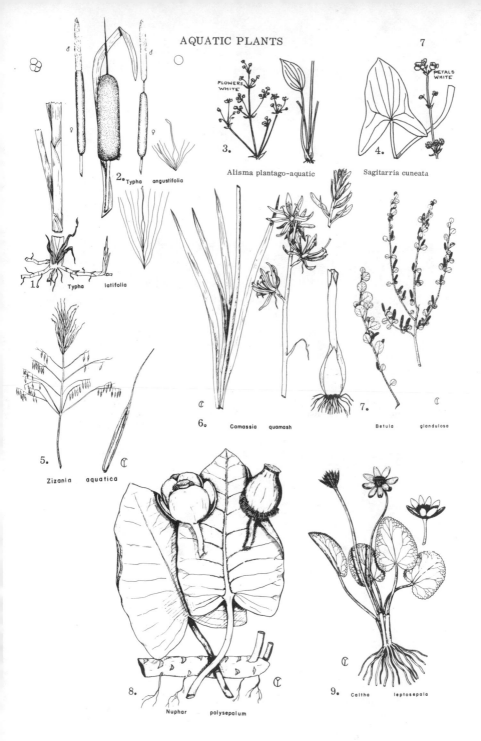

2. Typha angustifolia

3.

Alisma plantago-aquatic

FLOWERS WHITE

Sagitarria cuneata

PETALS WHITE

1. Typha latifolia

5.

Zizania aquatica

6. Camassia quamash

7.

Betula glandulosa

8.

Nuphar polysepalum

9. Caltha leptosepala

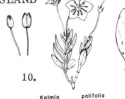

**T**
**Marsh**
**Str. Wd.**

10. BOG LAUREL (Kalmia polifolia). A small evergreen shrub, 1-3' tall; leaves 1/2-1" long, opposite, oblong to oval, leathery, green above, whitish below, margins inrolled; flowers pinkish-red, conspicuously saucer-shaped, about 1/2-3/4" broad, several borne on stalks from the tips of the branches; fruit a small globose capsule. Bogs.

10.

Kalmia          polifolia

OTHER PLANTS FOUND IN AQUATIC HABITATS INCLUDE: 25, annual bluegrass; 81, western blue flag; 80, black twinberry; 130, bunchberry; 87 , cow parsnip; 132, birdsbill; 148, western bistort.

------------------------------------------------------------

## GRASSLAND

Grasses in the Rocky Mountain Region occur predominately in the meadows with sedges or are associated with herbaceous or shrubby cover under the major woodland and coniferous forest communities. The meadows are found from medium to high elevations in the mountains or appear as openings in the timber or above timber line, as well as along the margins of streams, lakes and ponds from low to high altitudes. Many of these meadows are important habitats for animals.

Photo courtesy Canadian Wildlife Service, D. Munro.

------------------------------------------------------------

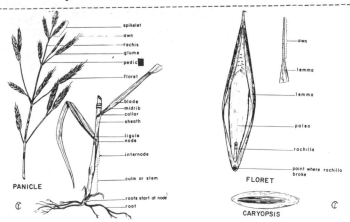

PANICLE

spikelet
awn
rachis
glume
pedicel
floret
blade
midrib
collar
sheath
ligule
node
internode
culm or stem
roots start at node
root

awn
lemma
lemma
palea
rachilla
point where rachilla broke

FLORET

CARYOPSIS

### PARTS OF TYPICAL GRASS

To help you identify grasses, the picture to the left shows the names of the parts. The picture on the right shows the parts of a grass floret.

## GRASSES

11. CRABGRASS (Digitaria sanguinalis). Spreading and branching annual, decumbent at the base with stems from 1-3' high, often rooting at the lower nodes; leaf blades hairy, the sheaths velvety or shaggy hairy; racemes 2-6" long with usually 3-7 branches borne finger-like on the terminal end or often with 1-2 whorls; spikelets in pairs, fertile lemma pale grayish. Noxious weed in towns, but excellent forage.

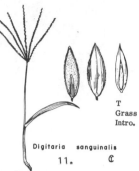

T
Grass
Intro.

Digitaria   sanguinalis

11.      C

12. BARNYARD GRASS (Echinochloa crusgalli). Coarse annual with erect or decumbent stems; 2-5' tall, sheaths hairless; panicle 4-8" long; spikelets green to purplish; awns mostly about 1/4" up to 1" or more in length. Weed in moist ground. Some value for forage if abundant.

T
Grass
Intro.

12.

Echinochloa    crusgalli

13. YELLOW FOXTAIL (Setaria lutescens). Erect to prostrate annual with stems 1-3' tall; leaf blades flat, sheaths smooth; ligules hairy, sheaths flattened; panicle cylindrical, spike-like, 1-4" long, the bristles appearing a golden-yellow color, 5-20 in a cluster, some 2-3 times as long as the spikelet, lemmas exposed, finely, sharply, cross-corrugated. Common introduced weed in fields and waste places. Palatable to stock.

T
Grass
Intro.

14. NEEDLE AND THREAD (Stipa comata). Erect rather stout perennial bunchgrass with stems 1-4' tall; leaf blades flat or inrolled, 4-12" long; ligule 1/8" long, thin; panicle narrow, 4-8" long, often included in the sheath especially toward the base; lemma about 1/4" long, pale yellowish-brown at maturity, body sparsely hairy at least below; awn 4 6" long, very slender and wavy, obscurely two-jointed. Good early forage.

T
Grass
Jun. Mah
Sage

15. TIMOTHY (Phleum pratense). Stems 1-4' tall, all tufted from a swollen bulb-like base; panicle spike-like, cylindrical 1-7" long, 1/5-1/3" wide; glumes hairy on the mid-vein, abruptly cut-off at tip; awns stout, about 1/24" long. Widely cultivated introduced grass; good forage.

T
Grass
Intro.

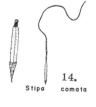

13.          C

Setaria      lutescens

14.      C

Stipa     comata

15.

Phleum     pratense

T
Grass
Meadow
Conif.

16. TUFTED HAIR GRASS (Deschampsia caespitosa). Tufted perennial, with stems 2-4' tall; leaves mostly basal, blades rough and flat, sheaths hairless; panicle open, drooping 4-10" long; spikelets 2-flowered, pale and shining or sometimes purplish, borne on the ends of slender branches.

AH
Grass
Meadow
Sub-Alp.

17. SPIKE TRISETUM (Trisetum spicatum). Tufted perennial with unbranched stem, 6-18" tall, leaf blades and sheaths finely hairy to hairless; panicle dense, spike-like, shining, pale yellow to purplish, 1 1/2-6" long; spikelet 2-3 flowered, awn attached 1/3 way below the apex of lemma, widely spreading but twisted at least when dry, 1/6-1/4" long. Good forage.

T
Grass
Conif.
Meadow
Sage

18. JUNE GRASS (Koeleria cristata). Erect perennial bunchgrass, 1-2' high; leaf blades flat or inrolled, 1-4" long, more or less roughly hairy; sheaths hairless to rough-hairy; panicle pale shining, sometimes purplish, densely flowered, 2-5" long, often interrupted, branches appressed; the spikelets 2-4-flowered, lemmas shiny, rarely short-awned. Good forage.

T
Grass
Str. Wd.
Intro.

*19. WILD OATS (Avena fatua). Stout erect annual with stems 1-3' tall; leaves flat, numerous, rough to touch; panicle open, usually 3-flowered; lemma clothed with reddish-brown or whitish hairs; awned from the back with stout stiff bent bristle, twisted below, 1 1/2" long. Good forage.

T
Grass
Intro.

20. TALL OATGRASS (Arrhenatherum elatius). Loosely tufted erect perennial with stems 3-4 1/2' tall; blades flat, rough, 1/4-1/2" wide; panicle narrow, pale, and shiny; yellowish-green to purplish, 6-12" long; spikelets 2-flowered, the lower with stamens only, the upper with both stamens and pistil, and a twisted bent conspicuous awn, borne on the back near the base. Widespread, introduced weed, cultivated as meadow grass.

T
Grass
Meadow
Conif.

21. CALIFORNIA WILD OATGRASS (Danthonia californica). Smooth stemmed perennial, 2-3' tall; leaf blades rough above, narrow and inrolled; the sheaths hairless or hairy only at the throat; panicle open, bearing 2-5 fairly large, several-flowered spikelets; pedicels spreading or reflexed; awns twisted and abruptly-bent, the terminal segment 1/4-1/2" long. Open meadows, woods and streamsides. Good forage.

T
Grass
Sage

22. BLUE GRAMA (Bouteloua gracilis). Densely tufted perennial with erect stems, usually 8-20" tall; leaves basal, flat and often curly; spikes borne in racemes usually about 1-3 per stalk, about 1-2" long; spikelets one-sided, numerous, up to 80 in number; awns slender. Very important forage on the plains.

T
Grass
Conif.

23. SANDBERG BLUEGRASS (Poa secunda). (Not illustrated.) Erect leafy tufted perennial; stems slender, 1-2' tall; leaf blades short and soft, mostly folded; panicle narrow, 1-4" long; 2-4 flowered spikelets. Forage.

TC
Grass
Conif.
Str. Wd.

24. KENTUCKY BLUEGRASS (Poa pratensis). Slender erect somewhat tufted perennial with creeping rootstocks; stems smooth, 1-3' tall; leaf blades narrow, abruptly pointed, flat or folded; panicle 2-8" long, open pyramid-shaped; lower branches ascending or spreading, often in a whorl of 5, 1-3" long, bearing spikelets mostly about the middle; spikelet 3-5 flowered; floret cobwebby at base. Good pasture and lawn grass.

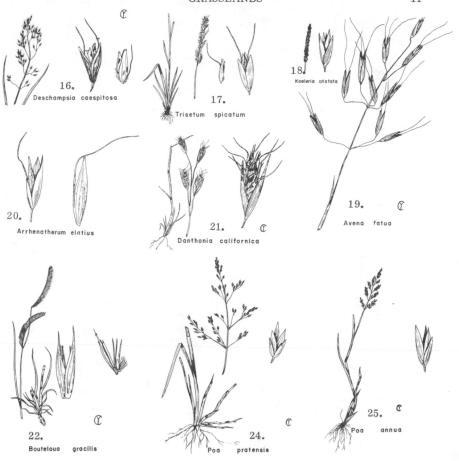

16. Deschampsia caespitosa

17. Trisetum spicatum

18. Koeleria cristata

19. Avena fatua

20. Arrhenatherum elatius

21. Danthonia californica

22. Bouteloua gracilis

24. Poa pratensis

25. Poa annua

25. ANNUAL BLUEGRASS (Poa annua). Low spreading bright green annual with flattened stems, 2-8" tall, often decumbent and forming mats, sometimes rooting at the lower nodes; leaf blades soft and lax; the spikelets 3-6 flowered, crowded in a panicle 1-3" long; lemmas keeled, not webbed, but hairy at the base. A troublesome weed; poor forage.

26. Poa bulbosa

26. BULBOUS GLUEGRASS (Poa bulbosa). Perennial, often tufted, from a bulbous base; 1-2' tall stems; leaf blades flat or loosely inrolled, sheaths hairless, panicle pyramidal, 2-3" long, florets change to bulblets, becoming dark purplish at least at base; spikelets 5-flowered, when unaltered; lemmas cob webby at base.

T
Grass
Conif.
Water
Str. Wd.
Intro.

TC
Grass
Intro.

27. TALL MANNAGRASS (Glyceria elata). Tall smooth succulent perennial with stems 2-6' tall; blades roughish, lax, thin, 1/4-1/2" wide, 8-16" long; panicle loose and open, 6-12" long, branches naked below, spreading, lower often reflexed; spikelets usually 6-8 flowered, oblong in shape. Wet meadows, streamsides, moist woods. Valuable forage.

T
Grass
Conif.
Meadow

28. SIX WEEKS FESCUE (Festuca octoflora). Slender erect annual grass, 4-16" tall, often forming tufts; leaves mostly basal; panicle narrow, 1-6" long; spikelets about 1/4-1/3" long, densely 5-13 flowered; usually one stamen. The most flowers per spikelet of any annual fescue. Poor forage.

T
Grass
Sage
Jun-Mah.

29. BLUE-BUNCH FESCUE (Festuca idahoensis). Densely tufted and erect perennial bunchgrass, 12-36" high; leaves numerous, mostly basal, stiff and rough to touch; panicle narrow, 4-8" long, rough; spikelets 4-6 flowered, 3 stamens; awns 1/12-1/6" long. Very fine forage grass.

T
Grass
Sage
Conif.
Jun-Mah.

30. CALIFORNIA BROME GRASS (Bromus carinatus). Coarse annual or biennial with erect stems, usually 1-4' tall; leaf blades flat and hairy, the sheaths velvety with soft hairs; panicle elongated pyramidal, somewhat narrow, often drooping, mostly 6-12" long; spikelets generally 6-10 flowered; awns conspicuous, 1-3" long. Too coarse to be good forage.

T
Grass
Conif.
Meadow
Jun. Mah.

31. DOWNY BROME GRASS (Bromus tectorum). Slender erect annual grass 6-24" tall; panicle open, branches spreading and drooping, 2-6" long, often purplish; blades and sheaths softly hairy; awns about 1/2" long. Dry places. Poor forage, except the early growth has some grazing value.

T
Grass
Conif.
Str. Wd.
Jun-Mah.

32. DARNEL (Lolium temulentum). Erect annual with stems 2-3' tall; leaf blades rough on upper surface, 4-10" long, flat, tapering at tip; spike 4-10" long; spikelets 4-7 flowered; first glume absent, except in terminal spikelets, the second equal or exceeding the florets; lemmas awnless, or short awned. Widespread introduced weed; considered poisonous.

TC
Grass
Intro.

33. ITALIAN RYEGRASS (Lolium multiflorum). Stout erect perennial, 2-3' tall; leaf blades light green, flat, 4-12" long; sheaths hairless or rough-hairy; spike flattened, 6-12" long, often roughened below; spikelets placed edgewise to flowering stem; 10-20 flowered; first glume wanting except in terminal spikelet, the second shorter than the florets; at least the upper lemmas awned. Introduced weed. Excellent forage grass.

TC
Grass
Intro.

34. BLUEBUNCH WHEATGRASS (Agropyron spicatum). Densely-tufted bunchgrass, often bluish in color, 12-36" tall; leaf blades narrow, usually inrolled, hairless below, slightly hairy above, leaf sheaths not hairy; spike slender, 2-4" long, the axis continuous, not breaking up at maturity; spikelets 3-6 flowered; awns sharply bent backwards. Good forage.

T
Grass
Conif.
Rocks

*35. WESTERN RYE GRASS (Elymus glaucus). Variable erect perennial with stems 2-4' high; leafy, blades flat, rough on both sides, 1/6-5/8" wide, 4-12" long; spike erect, narrow or rarely nodding, 2-8" long, usually greenish, sometimes purplish; spikelets 3-6 flowered, borne in pairs at the nodes; lemmas rough near the tip, with an awn 1 or 2 times the length of the body. Fair for grazing purposes. Grain edible if baked.

T
Grass
Conif.

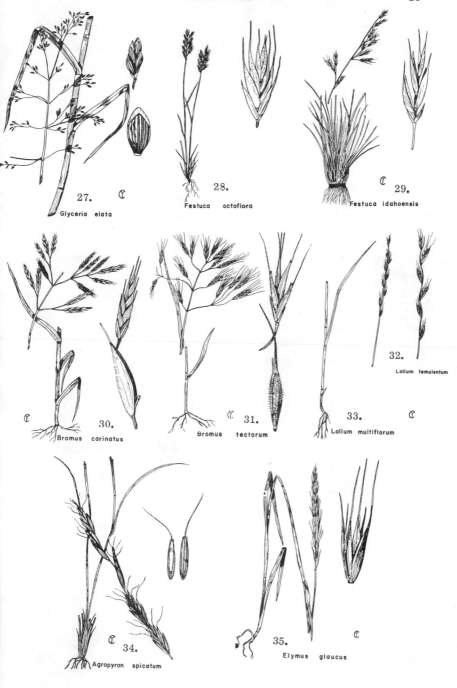

27. Glyceria elata

28. Festuca octoflora

29. Festuca idahoensis

30. Bromus carinatus

31. Bromus tectorum

32. Lolium temulentum

33. Lolium multiflorum

34. Agropyron spicatum

35. Elymus glaucus

*36. GIANT WILD RYE GRASS (Elymus cinereus). Coarse erect robust perennial with stems 3-7' tall; blades flat, 1/4-3/4" wide, very rough-hairy to hairless; spike dense, 4-12" long, sometimes the spike is branched; glumes narrow and awn-like; lemmas awnless. Grows in large clumps; limited for forage. Grain roasted and pounded into flour by Indians.

T
Grass
Meadow
Jun-Mah.

*37. CANADA WILDRYE (Elymus canadensis). Erect rather tall perennial with stems 2-5' tall, leaf blades flat, rough-hairy, 1/4-3/4" wide, leaf sheaths hairless or rarely finely hairy; spike bristly, dense, nodding 4-10" long, spikelets 2-4 at a node, 2-5 flowered; glumes narrow, rough; awn bent and cruved, 3/4-1" long. Along streams, lakesides and sandy soils. Inferior forage except when young.

T
Grass
Meadow

38. SQUIRRELTAIL GRASS (Sitanion hystrix). Tufted erect perennial with stiff stems 4-12" high, leaf blades rough-hairy or hairless, flat or becoming inrolled; prominently veined; spikes break up at maturity, 2-3" long, very brushy-bristly; spikelets 2 at each joint of the flowering stem; each spikelet has 2 to few flowers; glumes entire or split at base into 2 parts; awn of lemma about 1 1/2" long. Dry hillsides and sagebrush plains. Inferior forage, except when young. Spikelets may injure noses of stock.

TCH
Grass
Meadow
Conif
Rocks
Sub-Alp.
Jun. Mah

HERBS

*39. WILD HYACINTH(Brodiaea grandiflora). Stem 8-20" tall; leaves 2 to several, linear, shorter than the stem; umbel 6-14 flowered, bright blue; stamens 6, alternating, of 2 different lengths, inner with filaments (stalks) very broad below, about equaling the anthers. Moist rocky slopes, grassy hillsides, and open woods. B. C. to Mont., Utah to California.

T
Grass

40. CAT'S EAR (Calochortus elegans). Stem slender, 2-6" tall, with a small bulb at the base, leaf longer than the stem, flowers small, in umbels, greenish-white, tinged with purple; petals white, a purple blotch at the base; gland narrow, crescent-shaped, fringed; fruit nodding, strongly 3-angled. Moist woods and shady mountain slopes. Wash. to Idaho.

TC
Grass

41. GRASS WIDOWS (Sisyrinchium douglasii). Stem 6-18" tall from a cluster of thickened roots; stem leaves thick, shorter than the sheaths, basal leaves scale-like; flowers 1-8, pinkish-purple, only a few present at blossoming time; filaments united into a tube; fruit a globose capsule. Meadows and grassy hillsides. B. C. to Idaho and Utah.

T
Grass
Meadow

42. NELSON'S LARKSPUR (Delphinium nelsonii). Low erect perennial; stem 4-12" tall from a cluster of globose tubers; leaves few, 1-2" wide, palmately divided into 3-5 wedge-shaped divisions, these 3-lobed; flowers purple, 5-20, borne in racemes; follicles (pods) finely hairy or smooth when mature, divergent (spreading). Poisonous to stock.

T
Grass
Conif.
Str. Wd.
Asp. Wdl.
Sage
Meadow

43. NORTHERN BEDSTRAW (Galium boreale). Stems 6-24" tall, square, much-branched; leaves narrow, in a whorl of 4, conspicuously 3-veined, 1/2-11/2" long, obtuse, smooth or rough-hispid; flowers small, yellowish to white, very numerous, in dense pyramidal (or rarely flattened) cymes; petals 4, united below; fruits in 2's, becoming glabrous.

T
Grass
Conif.
Str. Wdl.
Asp. Wdl.
Sage

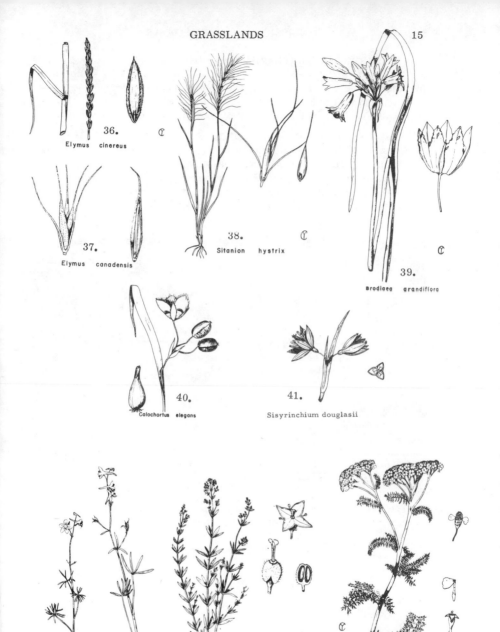

36. Elymus cinereus

37. Elymus canadensis

38. Sitanion hystrix

39. Brodiaea grandiflora

40. Calochortus elegans

41. Sisyrinchium douglasii

42. Delphinium nelsonii

43. Galium boreale

44. Achillea millefolium

**44. YARROW (Achillea millefolium var. lanulosa).** An erect perennial herb with stems 1-2' tall; herbage grayish, densely white-hairy; leaves pinnately very finely divided into numerous narrow segments; upper leaves much reduced; ray flowers white to rose, disc flowers yellow and inconspicuous, heads arranged in flat-topped clusters. Dry ground.

TCH
Grass
Sage
Sub-alp.

OTHER PLANTS FOUND IN THE GRASSLAND INCLUDE:

Shrubs: 52, big sage; 53, silver sagebrush;73, choke cherry; 97, small Oregon grape; and the shrubs and trees mentioned under Meadows below.

Herbs: 6 common camas; 59, blazing star; 62, arrow-leaved balsam root; 60, desert primrose; 63, blanket flower; 56, bronze bells; 125, mint-leaf bee-balm; and the herbs mentioned under Meadows below.

Meadow in Glacier Nat. Park; courtesy National Park Service.

## MEADOWS

The mountain meadows have similar plants to the lower grasslands, but are noted particularly for the following plants.

### TREES AND SHRUBS

**45. MOUNTAIN ALDER (Alnus tenuifolia).** A small tree or shrub 6-25' tall; leaves ovate, rounded at the tip, deeply double-toothed and lobed; staminate flowers in long drooping catkins; pistillate catkins short, erect and spike-like; fruit a nutlet with narrow transparent margins; peduncles stout, shorter than the cones. Stream banks, lake shores and meadows.

TC
Meadow
Conif.

**46. ROCKY MOUNTAIN MAPLE (Acer glabrum).** A small tree or shrub 6-30' tall with thin ashy-gray bark; leaves 3-5 lobed, 2-4" long, bright green above, paler beneath; flowers small, greenish-yellow, 5-15 in a corymbose cluster; fruit a double samara, the wings ascending. In moist woods and streamsides in mountains.

TC
Meadow
Conif.
Str. Wd.

47.  WHITE BOG ORCHID (Habenaria dilatata).  Stem leafy, 6-30"tall; T
leaves lance-shaped to linear, reduced upward; flowers white in a rather Meadow
dense terminal spike-like raceme; sepals and petals similar; lip spread- Str. Wd.
ing; spur nearly equalling the lip in length, slightly club-shaped.  Bogs.

48.  TALL WHITE BOG ORCHID (Habenaria dilatata var. leucostachys). TC
Like the above except the spur is about 2 times the length of the lip and the Meadow
plant is more robust.  Moist situations, often at higher elevations than the Str. Wd.
typical form.  Alaska to western Mont., Nevada to California. Sub-Alp.

49.  MONKSHOOD (Aconitum columbianum).  Stem 2-4' tall; all leaves TC
palmately-lobed or divided, 3-5 times; flowers purplish-blue in a loosely Meadow
few flowered raceme; the upper sepal forms a hood which encloses the Str. Wd.
upper 2 hooded petals; fruit of 2-6 follicles (pods).     Moist areas. Conif.

50.  FRINGED GENTIAN (Gentiana thermalis).  (Not illustrated.)  The
stems 6-16" tall, often several from the base, each peduncle bearing a T
single showy flower; leaves opposite, in pairs, the upper sessile, broadly Meadow
linear to lanceolate, up to 2 inches long, the basal petioled, oblanceolate, Str. Wd.
about 1" long; flowers bluish-purple, tube 1 1/2-2" long, the flaring lobes
conspicuously fringed; fruit a capsule.   Meadows in the mountains.

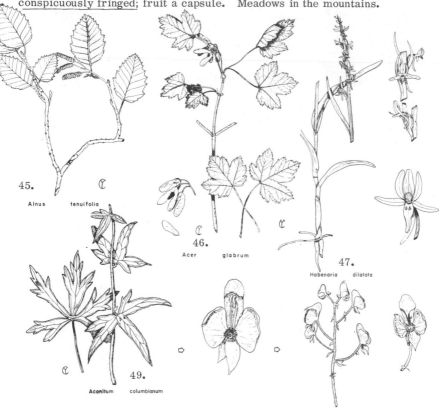

45.

Alnus        tenuifolia

46.

Acer      glabrum

47.

Habenaria      dilatata

49.

Aconitum     columbianum

OTHER PLANTS FOUND IN THE MEADOW HABITAT (besides those in the grasslands) INCLUDE:

Trees: 66, quaking aspen; 68, black cottonwood.

Shrubs: 7, bog birch; 77, red osier dogwood; 70 golden currant; 78, blue elderberry; 79, black elderberry; 98, swamp currant.

Grasses: most of those listed under grasslands.

Herbs: 6, common camas; 9, heart-leaved marsh-marigold; 123, columbine; 124, meadow-rue; 127, fireweed; 81, western blueflag; 120, spring beauty; 145, green false hellebore; 148, western bistort; 126, wood violet; 122, blue columbine; 132, birdsbill; 133, cat's breeches; 87, cow parsnip; 86, rose hollyhock; 134, Indian paintbrush; 152, Lewis' monkeyflower; 154, mountain valerian; 155; mountain daisy; 88, spearhead ragwort.

Photo of sagebrush habitat, courtesy of Southern Pacific Company.

## SAGEBRUSH HABITAT

There are several sagebrush communities in the Rocky Mountains. These are readily recognized by the general grayish appearance of the dominant plants which give the community its name. The big sagebrush community covers many miles at both medium and high elevations. It may appear as a conspicuous invader in almost any of our communities. There are many plants associated with this species. Antelope brush normally occurs here especially on higher drier sandy ridges. Sometimes silver sage will invade an area, particularly along the margins. Many species of grasses appear here shaded by larger shrubs. Silver sage also forms a conspicuous community, usually occurring closer to water or where there is a constant supply of moisture available. This community, like the former, has many associated grasses growing beneath it as ground cover.

51.  ANTELOPE BRUSH (Purshia tridentata).  Erect and  diffusely branched shrub, 3-9' tall with ashy-gray or brownish bark; leaves thickish, wedge-shaped in outline, 1/4-3/4" long, 3-lobed at apex; flowers yellow, 2/3" across, usually solitary, sometimes several in the axils of the leaves; fruit a spindle-shaped achene, solitary or in pairs.  Dry areas.

T
Sage
Jun. Mah.

52.  BIG SAGE (Artemisia tridentata).   Shrub 1-10' tall with woody branching trunk and dark brown or grayish shreddy bark; herbage aromatic; leaves silvery-gray, wedge-shaped, mostly 3-toothed at the tip; flowers 4-9, borne in small heads subtended by a cup-like base of  overlapping scales; head greenish-yellow, turning brown with age.  Dry areas.

TCH
Sage
Grass
Jun. Mah.
Str. Wd.
Asp. Wdl.

53.  SILVER SAGEBRUSH (Artemisia cana).  Shrub usually 1-3' tall, finely white hairy throughout; stems branching, forming a dense  clump; leaves silky-hairy, 1-2" long, linear, tips pointed, usually entire, sometimes 1-2 toothed or lobed; flower heads numerous, yellowish, borne in close elongated clusters, 5-12" long,  1-2" wide; flowers 6-20 in each head.  Moist plains, prairies and valleys in the mountains.

TC
Sage
Asp. Wdl.
Grass
Str. Wd.
Jun. Mah.

## GRASS

54.  COLUMBIA NEEDLEGRASS (Stipa columbiana).  Tufted erect perennial with hairless stems 2-4' tall; leaf blades narrow, flat or inrolled; sheaths hairless; panicle narrow 2-6" long, often purplish; glumes roughened, about 1/4" long; awns 3/4-1" long, with 2 joints; lemma equally pubescent throughout.  Open woods, dry hillsides and plains.  Fine forage.

T
Sage
Meadow

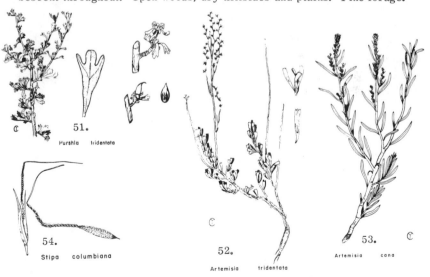

51.
Purshia  tridentata

54.
Stipa   columbiana

52.
Artemisia   tridentata

53.
Artemisia   cana

**55.  SEGO LILY (Calochortus nuttallii).** Stem 8-16" tall from a small coated bulb, sometimes bearing bulblets toward the base; leaves narrow, 1-2 basal; flowers showy, white to lavender-blue, 1-4 borne in a terminal umbel-like cluster; sepals and petals marked with a conspicuous red or purplish blotch; fruit a lance-shaped capsule 1-2" long. Dry grassy or brushy hillsides and flats.  S. E. Idaho to North Dakota and south.

T
Sage
Jun. Mah.

**56.  BRONZE BELLS (Fritillaria atropurpurea).** Stem slender, 6-24" tall from a fleshy-sealed bulb; leaves 6-14, narrow, generally scattered up the stem; flower purplish, spotted with yellow and white, bell-shaped and nodding; fruit a 6-angled, almost rectangular capsule. Dry slopes and grassy flats.  E. Oregon and Idaho to Nebraska and south.

T
Sage
Grass
Str. Wd.

**57.  BLUE FLAX (Linum Lewisii).** Stems 8-18" tall with a woody base, simple below and often branched above; leaves many, alternate, narrowly linear, about 1/2" long, pointed at the tip; flower 3/4-1" wide, few, pale blue, very showy, in a narrow cyme; fruit a globose capsule.

T
Meadow
Sage
Conif.
Asp. Wdl.

**58.  SMALL-FLOWERED LUPINE  (Lupinus argenteus parviflorus).** Stems erect, branched, glabrous to nearly silky; leaves compound palmate, leaflets 6-10, inverted lance-shaped, upper surface glabrous, with scattered or silky pubescence beneath; flowers small, 1/4-3/8" long, purplish-blue, borne in racemes 3 1/2-7" long; calyx not spurred; upper lip 2-toothed, lower lip entire; banner and wings glabrous, keel usually ciliate (with tiny hairs); fruit a densely-hairy pod (legume), 1/2-3/4" long. Hillsides, banks and open slopes.  E. Idaho to Wyo., Colo. to Utah.

TCH
Sage
Asp. Wds.
Conif.

**59.  BLAZING STAR (Mentzelia laevicaulis).** Plant coarse and rough; stems 1-3 1/2' tall, very stout, branching above; leaves lance-shaped to ovate lance-shaped, wavy-toothed to pinnatifid, rough-hairy; flowers showy, bright yellow, large, up to 3" across, borne in clusters of 2-3 at the ends of the branches; stamens yellow, many, very conspicuously exserted (protruding beyond) in clusters; fruit a cylindrical capsule, 1"- 1 1/2" long. Dry areas; e. Wash. to Idaho, Mont., Utah, Nevada.

T
Sage
Grass

**60.  DESERT PRIMROSE (Oenothera caespitosa).** Tufted perennial; stemless or nearly so, shaggy hairy to glabrous; leaves in a basal cluster, ovate to oblanceolate in outline, wavy margined, rarely pinnatifid, blades 1-4" long, on winged petioles about the same length; flowers white, becoming reddish with age, 1/2-3" broad, hypanthium (cup-shaped organ at base of flower) 2-4" long, narrowly funnel-form; fruit an oblong or linear capsule. Dry or rocky areas; Wash. to Montana and south.

T
Sage
Grass

**61.  FOXFIRE (Gilia aggregata).** Stems erect, 1-2' tall, usually unbranched from a biennial taproot; leaves divided or twice-divided into narrow segments, sticky hairy; basal leaves in a rosette, stem leaves alternate; flowers bright scarlet, salmon or rarely white in color, trumpet-like in shape, the tube 1/2-1" long; fruit a capsule. Rocky areas.

TC
Sage
Jun. Mah.
Conif.

**62.  ARROW-LEAVED BALSAM ROOT (Balsamorhiza sagittata).** The stems 1 1/2-2 1/2' tall, clustered at the base; leaves broadly arrow-head

T
Sage
Asp. Wdl.
Grass

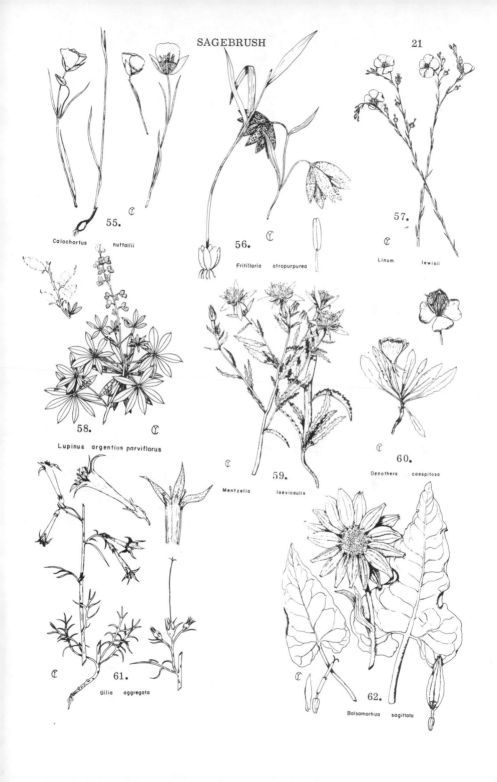

55.

Calochortus    nuttallii

56.

Fritillaria    atropurpurea

57.

Linum    lewisii

58.

Lupinus  argentius parviflorus

59.

Mentzelia    laevicaulis

60.

Oenothera    caespitosa

61.

Gilia    aggregata

62.

Balsamorhiza    sagittata

shaped, 3-8" long, covered with soft grayish-white hairs, margins wavy-entire; heads sunflower-like, each at end of stalk; a cluster of white-woolly bracts surround the flower base; ray flowers bright yellow, disc dark.

T
Sage
Grass

63. BLANKET FLOWER (Gaillardia aristata). Perennial; stems 8-16" tall, finely hairy, usually unbranched at the base, branching above; the leaves oblanceolate to oblong, entire or lobed and toothed; heads generally solitary, 2-3" in diameter, borne on long peduncles; ray flowers yellow (or with purple bases), about 13 in number, 3-toothed at the tips; disk flowers brownish-purple to yellow. Hillsides, prairies and plains.

OTHER PLANTS OF SAGEBRUSH HABITAT BUT DESCRIBED ELSEWHERE:

Trees and shrubs: 91, western yellow pine; 70, golden currant; 97, small Oregon grape.

Grasses: 14, needle and thread; 28, six weeks fescue; 34, bluebunch wheatgrass; 22 blue grama; 18, June-grass.

Herbs: 42, Nelson's larkspur; 43, northern bedstraw; 44, yarrow; 86, rose hollyhock; 85 wild geranium; 132, birdsbill; 136, Scotch bluebells; 137, showy fleabane; 133, cat's breeches; 147, sulphur flower; 148, western bistort.

Gaillardia    aristata

Mountain mahogany brush and juniper trees; courtesy Nat. Park Service.

## JUNIPER-MOUNTAIN MAHOGANY WOODLAND

Usually these woodlands can be recognized by the presence of Rocky Mountain juniper or mountain mahogany. The presence of either of these two species in association or in separate stands constitutes a type which is frequently seen on very dry sites. Sometimes these trees occupy low rounded hills or appear on rugged slopes which are cut by canyons and dry washes. The distribution is very spotty, as pure stands of mountain mahogany often alternate with pure stands of juniper. Normally this community is limited to the southern portion of our área.

64. ROCKY MOUNTAIN JUNIPER (Juniperus scopulorum). Slender tree, 20-45' tall with a rounded or scraggly crown; branches slender and hanging down at ends; bark reddish-brown or rarely grayish, scaly and roughened; leaves scale-like, margins entire, dark green, opposite each other, tightly appressed and sharply pointed at the tip, scarcely glandular but often covered with white powdery substance; berry globose, dark blue, with a light powdery bloom. Dry rocky slopes and rugged hillsides.

T
Jun. Mah.
Conif.

65. MOUNTAIN MAHOGANY (Cercocarpus ledifolius). Shrubs 4-12' tall or trees up to 20' in height; leaves evergreen, 1/2-2" long, elliptic, thick and leathery; flowers small, yellowish, usually in a cluster; fruits achenes with long feathery tails. Wash. to Montana and south.

T
Jun. Mah.

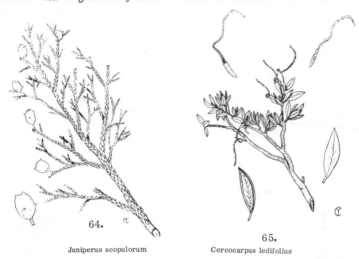

64.

Juniperus scopulorum

65.

Cercocarpus ledifolius

OTHER PLANTS FOUND IN THE JUNIPER-MOUNTAIN MAHOGANY WOODLAND INCLUDE:

Trees and shrubs: 91, western yellow pine; 51, antelope brush; 52, big sage; 53, silver sage.

Grass: 14, needle and thread; 28, six weeks fescue; 36, giant wild rye; 31, downy brome; 30, California brome; 34, bluebunch wheatgrass;      38, squirreltail grass.

Herbs: 55, sego lily; 61, foxfire.

------------------------------------------------------------
Photo of aspen woodland by Charles Yocom.
------------------------------------------------------------

## ASPEN WOODLAND

This community is made up almost entirely of groves of aspen (Populus tremuloides). The trees occupy dense stands on moist flats in stream valleys or occur in open stands on drier sloping hillsides. The understory consists of shrubs and herbs which are not conspicuously different from those found in other communities. However, the aspen groves form a very prominent part of the vegetation through much of the Rockies.

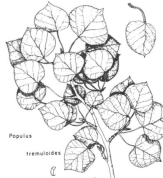

66. QUAKING ASPEN (Populus tremuloides). Usually a slender small graceful tree, 10-50' tall, with smooth light-green to whitish bark; leaves 1-2" wide, broadly heart-shaped to sub-orbicular, glabrous, pale green, palmately-veined, the margins finely regularly toothed or wavy, abruptly pointed at the tip; petioles slender, flattened laterally causing a fluttering of the leaves in the slightest wind; flowers of two kinds borne in catkins on different trees. Often forms dense pure stands.

TCH
Asp. Wdl.
Conif.
Str. Wd.
Meadow

Populus
tremuloides

OTHER PLANTS FOUND IN ASPEN WOODLAND INCLUDE: 66.
Shrubs: 52, big sage; 53, silver sagebrush; 80, black twinberry; 71, white-stemmed gooseberry; 97, small Oregon grape; 109, snowbrush.
Herbs: 6, common camas; 42, Nelson's larkspur; 43, northern bedstraw; 57, blue flax; 58, small-flowered lupine; 62, arrow-leaved balsam root; 84, sticky geranium; 85, wild geranium; 87 cow parsnip; 124, meadow-rue; 133, cat's breeches; 137, showy fleabane.

Photo of woodland along river by Dr. Charles Yocom.

## STREAMSIDE WOODLAND

This woodland is present along the many streams and rivers which occur throughout our area. It is dominated principally by cottonwoods and willows. Blue spruce is often scattered among the more mature cottonwoods in situations which are moist during the growing season. The understory consists of dense thickets of shrubs plus herbs and grasses.

### TREES AND SHRUBS

67.

Populus    angustifolia

67. NARROW-LEAF COTTON-WOOD (Populus angustifolia). Tall slender tree, 15-60' high, with greenish ascending branches; leaves thin, narrowly to broadly lance-shaped, green on both surfaces, 2-4" long, rounded at the base and gradually tapering to a blunt point at the tip, the margins with minute rounded teeth; staminate and pistillate catkins borne on separate trees. Along stream banks.

TC
Str. Wd.

68. BLACK COTTONWOOD (Populus trichocarpa). (Illustrated on page 27.) Large tree, 25-150' tall, with erect open branches; bark grayish-yellow to blackish and deeply furrowed; leaves shiny, ovate to lance-ovate, 2-5" long, abruptly pointed or tapering at tip, dark green on upper surface, the margins evenly-toothed, lighter greenish-brown beneath, pinnately-veined, at

T
Str. Wd.
Meadow

first hairy, later becoming glabrous; buds very resinous-sticky; petioles long, not flat; staminate and pistillate catkins borne on separate trees.

69. COLORADO BLUE SPRUCE (Picea pungens). Small or medium-sized tree, 50-100' tall, at first quite symmetrically cone-shaped, less so with age; branches rigidly horizonal and in layers; bark thick and scaly, pale to grayish-tinged with red; needles 3/4-1 1/8" long, scattered, blue-green with a whitish cast, sharply 4-angled, stiffly sharp pointed at the apex, falling when dry, leaving peg-like bases on the branchlets; cones 2 1/4-4" long, numerous, oblong-cylindrical, pendulous, light brown; scales with wavy margins and toothed tips. E. Idaho to Wyo. and south.

TC
Str. Wd.
Conif.

*70. GOLDEN CURRANT (Ribes aureum). Shrub 3-8' tall, almost glabrous throughout; leaves 1/2-2" wide, 3-5 lobed, wedge-shaped to heart-shaped at the base; flowers golden yellow, 1/4-3/4" long, cylindrical, flaring at the tip; edible berry light yellow to bright red, globose, 1/4" wide.

T
Str. Wd.
Meadow
Sage

*71. WHITE-STEMMED GOOSEBERRY (Ribes inerme). Shrub 2-6' tall with slender whitish smooth stems and 1-3 spines about 1/4" long, borne at the nodes; leaves roundish, 3/4" 1 1/2" wide, 3-5 lobed, sharply toothed, glabrous (smooth) on both surfaces, heart-shaped to wedge-shaped; flowers greenish or purplish, bell-shaped, 1-4 nodding peduncles (stalks); berry smooth reddish-purple to blackish, about 1/3" in diameter (dried and mixed with ground baked grain by Indians).

T
Str. Wd.
Asp. Wdl.
Conif.
Rocks

*72. SPALDING'S WILD ROSE (Rosa spaldingii). Slender erect shrub 2-6' tall with broad stiff straight prickles; leaves compound, rachis (central leaf stem) nearly glabrous; leaflets 1/3-2" long, the margins mostly simply toothed, usually glabrous (smooth) on both surfaces, if pubescent beneath not glandular; flowers pink, showy, 2-3" wide, often solitary, the calyx lobes minutely toothed; fruit bright red, globose, 1/2-3/4" in diameter. Open woods and thickets. Young buds edible.

T
Str. Wd.

*73. CHOKE CHERRY (Prunus virginiana var. demissa). Shrub or small tree, 4-20' tall; leaves ovate to elliptic, sometimes hairy on the lower veins, 1 1/2-4" long, pointed at the tip and rounded to heart-shaped at the base; flowers creamy-white, 1/4-1/2" wide, numerous, borne in cylindrical racemes, 2-6" long; fruit a globose dark-red to purplish black drupe (edible, best when cooked or mixed with other foods).

T
Str. Wd.
Grass
Conif.

*74. WILD CHERRY (Prunus emarginata). Bush or small tree 4-8' tall; leaves ovate to oval, usually rounded at the tip, pubescent or smooth beneath, finely toothed, 1-3" long; flowers creamy-white, borne in corymbs; fruit a bitter, dark-red drupe (cooked into jam or jelly).

TC
Str. Wd.
Conif.

75. BLACK HAWTHORN (Crataegus douglasii). Large shrub or small tree 5-25' tall, with spines 1/2-1" long; leaves 1-4" long, obovate, wedge-shaped at the base, margins lobed and doubly-toothed from the middle upward; flowers white in cymost clusters, about 1/2-2/3" across; fruit 1/3-1/2" in diameter (resembling tiny apples), bluish-black in color.

T
Str. Wd.

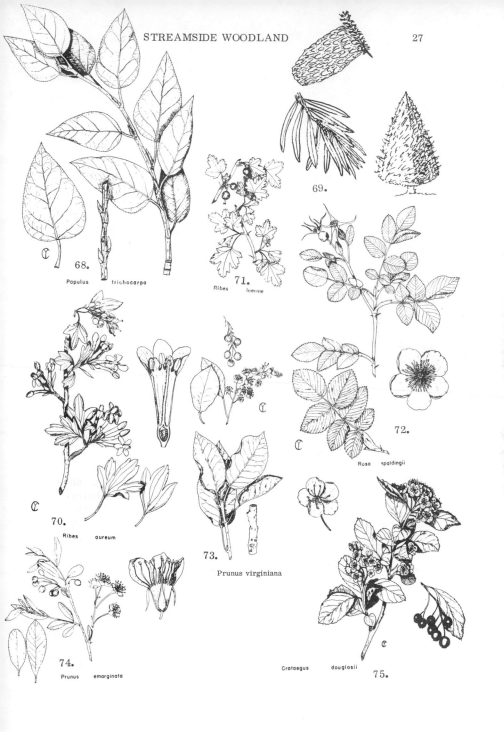

69.

68.

Populus    trichocarpa

71.

Ribes    inerme

72.

Rosa    spaldingii

70.

Ribes    aureum

73.

Prunus virginiana

74.

Prunus    emarginata

Crataegus    douglasii    75.

TC
Str. Wd.
Conif.

*76. CANADA BUFFALOBERRY (Elaeagnus canadensis). Slender un-armed shrub, with reddish-brown or grayish bark, stems 2-6' tall; leaves oblong or ovate, 1-2" long, rounded at the tip, sparingly stellate hairy and dull green above, densely silvery stellate (star-shaped rays) beneath, in-termingled with patches of rusty scales; flowers yellowish inside, brown-ish outside, inconspicuous in clusters at the nodes of the twigs, often ap-pearing before the leaves; fruit a small, ovoid, juicy, yellowish to bright red berry (edible). Moist open woods.

T
Str. WdL
Conif.
Meadow

77. RED-OSIER DOGWOOD (Cornus stolonifera). Shrub 4-15' tall, usually with reddish branches; leaves 2-4" long, ovate or egg-shaped, conspicuously ribbed beneath, dark green above, lighter below; flowers in flat clustered cymes, 1 1/2-2 1/2" across; petals tiny, 1/6" long, green-ish-white; fruit white or bluish tinged, nearly round, berry-like, about 1/4" wide, juicy, inedible. Thickets and stream banks.

T
Str. WdL
Conif.
Meadow

*78. BLUE ELDERBERRY (Sambucus coerulea). Shrub 5-20' high; leaflets 5-9, coarsely serrated, 1 1/2-5" long, pointed at the apex, inflo-rescence flat-topped; flowers small, cream-colored or whitish; fruit a dark blue berry with a dense white bloom, borne in clusters up to 12" across (edible, especially in pie or jelly). Moist woods, hillsides, etc.

TC
Str. WdL
Rocks
Meadow
Conif.

*79. BLACK ELDERBERRY (Sambucus racemosa var. melanocarpa). Shrub 3-10' tall; leaflets 5-7, ovate or elliptic, dark green, all sharply coarsely serrate, 2-5" long, abruptly long-pointed at the apex, more or less pubescent beneath, becoming glabrous with age; flowers tiny, cream-white in a dense rounded cluster, 1 1/2-3" in diameter; fruit a dark-pur-plish to black shiny berry, about 1/4-1/3" in diameter (edible, used for pies, jellies and jam). Open slopes, thickets, moist woods and meadows.

T
Str. WdL
Conif.
Asp. WdL
Marsh

80. BLACK TWINBERRY (Lonicera involucrata). Erect branching shrub 1-5' tall; leaves narrowly elliptic to ovate, 2-5" long, glossy green, margins entire; flowers yellow, short tubular, 1/2-3/4" long; fruit a shiny black berry, surrounded by 2 large leafy red bracts; berry inedible.

## HERBS

T.
Str. Wd.
Meadow
Marsh

81. WESTERN BLUE FLAG (Iris missouriensis). Stem 1-2' tall from a short rootstalk; leaves mostly basal; flowers violet-blue, showy, solitary or in an umbel-like cluster; style branches petal-like; fruit a 3-angled cap-sule. Wet meadows and swales.

T
Str. Wd.
Conif.

82. PURPLE CLEMATIS (Clematis columbiana). Semi-woody trailing or climbing vine; stems 3-12' long; leaves compound, 3-foliate, long-peti-oled (stemmed); leaflets ovate rounded or heart-shaped at the base, mar-gins entire or sparingly toothed; flowers nodding, solitary, purple or blue; achenes densely short-hairy with long feathery tails. Moist areas.

T
Str. Wd.

83. YELLOW PEA (Thermopsis montana). Perennial herb with erect stems, 1-2' tall, often branching, glabrous or minutely hairy; leaves com-pound, 3-foliate, long-petioled with leafy stipules, the leaflets ovate to

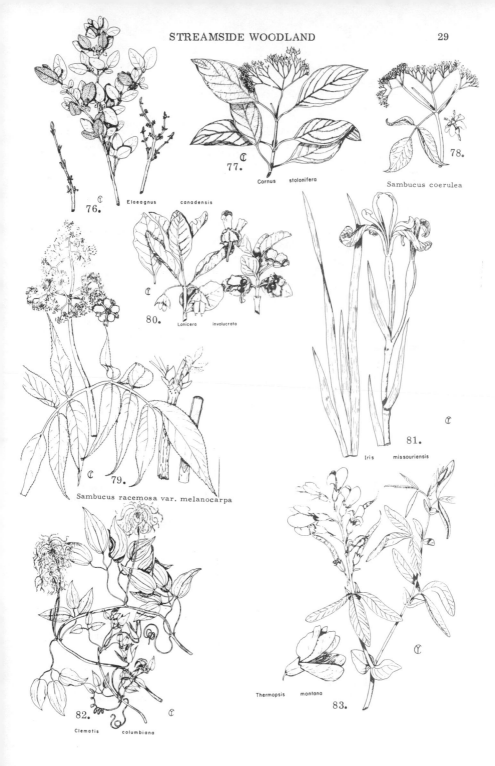

76. Elaeagnus canadensis

77. Cornus stolonifera

78. Sambucus coerulea

80. Lonicera involucrata

79. Sambucus racemosa var. melanocarpa

81. Iris missouriensis

82. Clematis columbiana

83. Thermopsis montana

obovate, 1 1/2-3" long, glabrous above, slightly hairy beneath; flowers bright yellow, nearly 1" long, borne in a showy many-flowered raceme; stamens 10, all separate; fruit a pod (legume), usually erect. Moist hillsides, slopes and streambanks. Wash to Mont. and south.

T
Str. Wd.
Asp. Wdl.
Conif.

84. STICKY GERANIUM (Geranium viscosissimum). Glandular sticky herb with stems 1-2' tall; leaves deeply cut almost to the midvein by 3-7 divisions, the lobes again sharply incised; flower 1-1 1/2" wide, light rose-pink to purple, borne in cymes; petals 5, with darker veins; the fruit splitting into 5 long-beaked parts at maturity. Prairies, thickets, woods.

T.
Str. Wd.
Asp. Wdl.
Sage

85. WILD GERANIUM (Geranium nervosum). Glabrous to hairy herb, simple at base, branching upward; stems 1-2' tall, with long straggly down-turned hairs on the internodes; leaves reniform in outline, 3-5" wide, palmately 5-7 lobed or divided, the divisions coarsely toothed and broadly wedge-shaped; flowers 1-1 1/2" wide, rose-purple, borne in close cymes; petals 5, with darker veins; fruit splitting into 5 long-beaked parts at maturity. Open hillsides, brushy slopes and streamsides.

T
Str. Wd.
Meadow
Sage

86. ROSE HOLLYHOCK (Sphaeralcea rivularis). Tall perennial herb; stems erect, 2-6' tall; leaves alternate, 2-5" long, the lower large and maple-like with 5-7 toothed lobes; upper leaves reduced in size; flowers pink, about 2" across, borne in clusters in the upper leaf axils; fruit of several parts, breaking up into equal sections. Moist areas.

T
Str. Wd.
Meadow
Marsh
Asp. Wdl.

*87. COW PARSNIP (Heracleum lanatum). Stem stout, 4-8' tall, hairy throughout; leaves divided into 3 leaflets, the leaflets broad, deeply toothed, 4-10" wide; flowers white, umbels 4-12" broad; fruit flattened, 1/4-1/2" long. Young leaves and stems edible. Moist places.

H
Str. Wdl
Meadow
Rocks

88. SPEAR-HEAD RAGWORT (Senecio triangularis). Stems slender, erect, 1-4' tall; leaves triangular, oblong ovate, margins sharply toothed, the blades 3-4" long, truncate at the base; heads in corymbs or cymes; flowers yellow, involucral bracts slender, acute, generally black-tipped, with minute hairs. Moist places, hillsides, meadows, streambanks.

COMMON PLANTS OF STREAMSIDE DESCRIBED ELSEWHERE:

Trees: 91, western yellow pine; 95, western red cedar; 96, western larch; 66, quaking aspen; 108, cascara.

Shrubs: 7, bog laurel; 10, bog birch; 46, Rocky Mountain maple; 52, big sage; 53, silver sage; 98, swamp currant; 100, ocean spray; 102, thimbleberry; 103, wood rose; 105, common service-berry; 106, devil's club; 112, mountain huckleberry; 141, dwarf juniper; 159, shrubby cinquefoil.

Grasses: 19, wild oats; 24 Kentucky bluegrass; 25, annual bluegrass; 31, downy brome grass.

Herbs: 6, common camas; 42, Nelson's larkspur; 43, northern bedstraw; 47 white bog orchid; 48, tall white bog orchid; 50, fringed gentian; 56, bronze bells; 119, fairy slipper; 49, monkshood; 127, fireweed; 132, birdsbill; 123, columbine; 134, Indian paintbrush; 137, showy fleabane; 147, sulphur flower; 152, Lewis' monkeyflower; 154, mountain valerian.

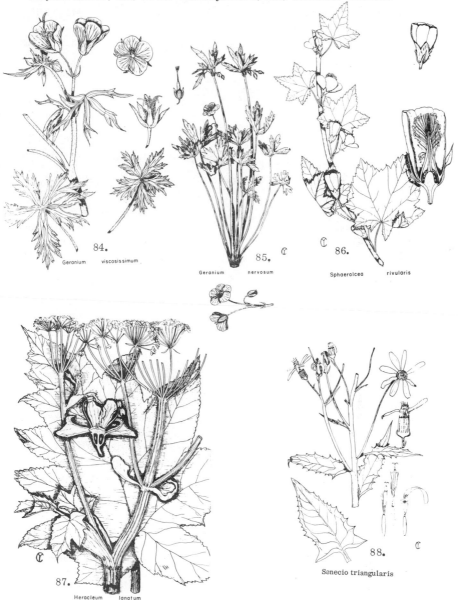

84. Geranium viscosissimum

85. Geranium nervosum

86. Sphaeralcea rivularis

87. Heracleum lanatum

88. Senecio triangularis

Coniferous forest in British Columbian Rockies; photo by Paul VanDyke.

## CONIFEROUS FORESTS

All of the forest communities found in our region are included here. At lower elevations the western yellowpine forest is dominant, forming in open park-like stands. This community is gradually replaced at higher altitudes by the Douglas fir forest, which in turn is succeeded by the cedar-hemlock forest still higher up where more moisture is present. This forest is supplanted by the spruce-fir forest in the sub-alpine area, while at timberline a fringe forest of white-bark pine usually occurs. Several other trees which are present in all of these forests in various degrees of abundance are larch, western white pine and lodgepole pine. The shade of the forest forms much cover in which darker colored animals and birds are found.

Fire destroys forests and sets up what is called plant succession. Usually the fire-killed forest is replaced first by herbs and grasses. Gradually such a temporary meadow-land is taken over by bushes, such as mountain mahogany and timbleberry. Next, fast-growing decid.ous trees such as quaking aspens gradually shade out the bushes. Last, coniferous trees begin to overtop the deciduous trees until the original coniferous forest comes back into dominance again. This process may take hundreds of years.

89.  WESTERN WHITE PINE (Pinus monticola).  Tall, slender tree, 75-150' tall; trunk 2-4' in diameter; bark grayish-purple to cinnamon color, broken into small squarish blocks; needles bluish-green with a whitish tinge, 2-4" long and borne 5 in a bundle; cones pendulous, cylindrical, 6-10" long, often slightly curved at base.  Idaho to Mont. & N.  *TC Conif.*

90.  LODGEPOLE PINE (Pinus contorta).  Slender tree, 60-80', often up to 150' high; trunk usually 2-3', rarely 5-6' in diameter; branches spreading, short, forming a narrow spire-like crown; bark thin, close, dark brown to light orange-brown, covered with small loose scales; needles are stout bright yellow-green, 1-3" long, borne 2 to a bundle; cones sub-cylindrical to oval, 1-2" long, very asymmetrical at the base, often clustered, yellow-brown at maturity; scales fairly thick, each with a stout, recurved, often deciduous prickle.  Rocky hillsides, valleys and plateaus.  *CH Conif.*

*91.  WESTERN YELLOW PINE (Pinus ponderosa).  Large tree, 50-200' tall, trunk 3-8' in diameter; bark on younger trees dark brown and deeply furrowed, 2-4" thick, later becoming light reddish-brown and irregularly divided into large scales or plates, the surface having a reddish exfoliated rubbed appearance; needles dark yellow-green, 5-10" long, borne in clusters at the ends of naked branches, usually 3 to a bundle; cones ovate, reddish-brown, 3-6" long, often several in a cluster; scales fairly narrow, the prickles broad, short-incurved at the tips, often deciduous.  Very common tree.  Edible sweet layer under bark in the spring.  *T Conif. Sage Jun-Mah. Str. Wd.*

92.  ENGELMANN SPRUCE (Picea engelmannii).  Large spire-shaped tree up to 150' tall, much shorter at higher elevations; bark light reddish  *CH Conif.*

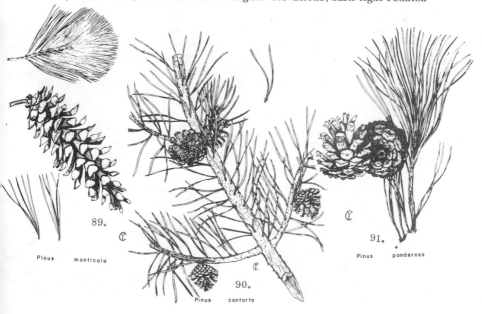

89.

Pinus  monticola

90.
Pinus  contorta

91.
Pinus  ponderosa

brown, thin, loose-scaly; branches spreading, short; needles scattered, 1-1 1/8" long, compressed 4-sided, flexible, but with sharp pointed tips, jointed near the base, falling when dry, the branches rough from the projecting bases of the needles; cones pendulous, oblong, 2-3" long; scales usually truncate, toothed or rarely entire at the tip. Mt. slopes & canyons.

**C**
**Conif.**

93. DOUGLAS FIR (Pseudotsuga menziesii). Large tree, 50-200' tall, 2-15' in diameter; bark dark ashy-brown, 5-15' thick, deeply furrowed with irregular ridges; needles 1/2-1 1/2" long, growing entirely around the branch, linear, soft, flat, pointed (not stiff) on tips, slightly grooved on top side, varying from yellowish-green to blue-green, paler on underside; cones 2-4" long, pendulous, brown to reddish-brown, the conspicuously 3-pointed bracts often exceeding the cone scales by 1/2". Good timber.

**H**
**Conif.**

94. ALPINE FIR (Abies lasiocarpa). Tall spire-shaped tree, 40-90' tall; trunk 1-3' in diameter; bark reddish-brown to grayish-white, 1/2 to 1 1/2" thick; needles flattened, strongly curved upward, 1-2" long, dark bluish-green, tinged with silver; cones cylindrical-oblong, dark purple, 2 1/2-4" long, borne erect on the twigs; scales broadly fan-shaped, falling one at a time, bracts included. Alpine slopes.

**C**
**Conif.**
**Str. Wd.**

95. WESTERN RED CEDAR (Thuja plicata). Large tree, 50-200' in height, with conical crown and drooping branches, arranged in flat sprays; trunk 3-10' in diameter, fluted at the base; bark fibrous-stringy, reddish-cinnamon brown to grayish on mature trees, deeply fissured; scale-like leaves 1/8-1/4" long, ovate and appressed; cones 1/4-1/2" long, brownish, narrowly ovoid, of about 3-6 pairs of elliptic scales. Moist places.

**TC**
**Conif.**
**Str. Wd.**

96. WESTERN LARCH (Larix occidentalis). Large tree, 50-90' tall, with a narrow open crown; trunk 6-8' in diameter; bark deeply furrowed at base, reddish brown with large scaly plates; needles flatly triangular, 1-2" long, soft, borne in tufted clusters of 12-30 on the branches, turning yellow with first frost and falling off; cones 1-1 1/2" long, oblong, bracts exceeding the scales. Moist bottoms, benches and mountain slopes.

## SHRUBS

**T**
**Conif.**
**Asp. Wdl.**
**Sage**
**Grass**

*97. SMALL OREGON GRAPE (Berberis repens). Low sub-shrub, 4-10" tall; stem often reclining or creeping; leaves 3-10" long, clustered at the base; leaflets 3-7, broadly ovate 1-2" long, margins obscurely bristle-toothed; flowers yellow, borne in racemes; fruit a waxy blue berry.

**CH**
**Conif.**
**Str. Wd.**
**Meadow**
**Rocks**

*98. SWAMP CURRANT (Ribes lacustre). Stems prostrate or ascending, 3-5' tall, armed with spines and numerous bristly prickles; leaves 1-2 1/2" broad, 3-7 lobed, the lobes incised, glabrous or nearly so; flowers 1/4" wide, greenish to purplish, borne in a 5-15 flowered drooping raceme; stamens very short; berries black, 1/4" in diameter, bearing weak gland-tipped hairs, edible. Moist places.

**T**
**Conif.**

*99. MALLOW NINEBARK (Physocarpus malvaceus). Erect or spreading shrub, 3-6' tall; leaves 1-2" long, round to subcordate at the base, all

broadly ovate to roundish in outline, shallowly 3-5 lobed; flowers whitish-
cream, borne in a few to many flowered hemispherical corymb; stamens
conspicuous, 25-30; fruits small follicles about 1/5" long.  Greens edible.

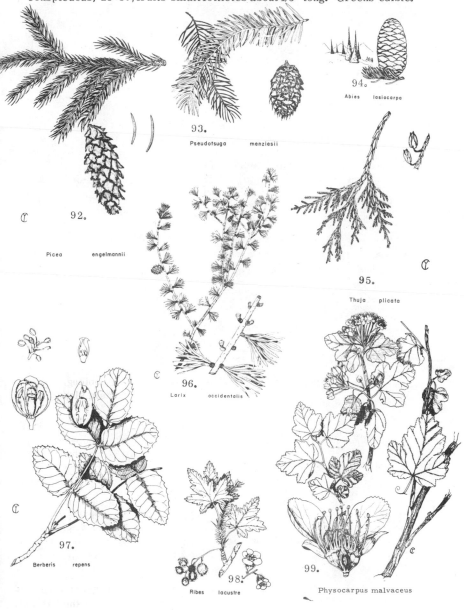

94.

Abies    lasiocarpa

93.

Pseudotsuga    menziesii

92.

Picea    engelmannii

95.

Thuja    plicata

96.

Larix    occidentalis

97.

Berberis    repens

98.

Ribes    lacustre

99.

Physocarpus malvaceus

T
Conif.
Str. Wd.

**100. OCEAN SPRAY (Holodiscus discolor).** Shrubs 3-8' tall,   erect; leaves triangular-ovate, toothed or lobed, usually truncate at base, minutely hairy beneath, green above; flowers creamy-white in large foamy pyramid-shaped panicles; fruits, 1-seeded hairy follicles.

TC
Conif.

**101. WHITE SPIRAEA   (Spiraea betulifolia).** Low shrub, 1-3' tall; leaves ovate, oval or obovate, 1-2 1/2" long, glabrous, alternate, the lower portion entire, the upper half coarsely toothed;   flowers white,   minute, borne in dense flat-topped clusters (corymbs), 2-4" wide, on the ends of leafy stems; stamens conspicuously exserted; pistils mostly 5, becoming dry non-inflated follicles at maturity.   Roadsides, open woods.

TC
Conif.
Str. Wd.

**\*102. THIMBLE BERRY (Rubus parviflorus).** Stems 2-5' tall,  no prickles present; leaves large, cordate, palmately 5-lobed, 3-8" wide, unevenly toothed; flowers large, white, 1 1/2-2" wide in a loose   terminal corymb; fruit juicy red to scarlet, the druplets separating and falling when ripe.   Along streams and in moist places.    Berries edible when red.

TC
Conif.
Str. Wd.

**103. WOOD ROSE (Rosa gymnocarpa).** Stems erect, 1-4' tall, woody with needle-like prickles; leaves compound divided into 5-7 leaflets; leaflets round-ovate to elliptic, 1/4-1" long, doubly serrated with gland-tipped teeth; flowers 3/4-1" wide, pink in color with a whitish base; fruit bright red, usually elliptical in shape, calyx lobes deciduous.   Mont. & Idaho N.

TC
Conif.

**104. ROCKY MOUNTAIN-ASH (Sorbus scopulina).** Shrub 3-12' tall; leaflets 11-13, elliptic to oblong lanceolate, 1 1/2-2 1/2" long, sharp-pointed at the apex, margins sharply toothed almost to the base, upper surface dark shiny green; flowers numerous (80-200), borne in a dense flat-topped cyme, 3 1/2-6" wide; fruit a bright orange-red   berry-like   pome, about 1/3" in diameter.   Canyons and wooded hillsides.

T
Conif.
Str. Wd.

**\*105. COMMON SERVICE-BERRY (Amelanchier florida).** Shrub 5-15' tall; leaves 1/2-2" long, oval or roundish, toothed above the middle, tips sharply pointed; flowers white, in few to 15 flowered racemes; fruit is a roundish bluish-black berry-like pome, about 3/8" in diameter, edible.

TC
Conif.
Str. Wd.

**106. DEVIL'S CLUB (Oplopanax horridum).** Straggly shrub, thickly armed with numerous stout yellow prickles; stems thick, 2-6' high; leaves large, palmately 3-7 lobed, the lobes unevenly sharply   toothed,   4-12" wide, prickly on the petioles and veins; flowers small, greenish-white, in small umbels, arranged terminally in large dense panicles; fruit a scarlet, laterally compressed berry.   Moist woods, Mont. to Ore. and north.

TC
Conif.

**107. MOUNTAIN LOVER (Pachystima myrsinites).** Evergreen shrub, 1-3' tall, glabrous (smooth) throughout; stems branching profusely; oval to obovate leaves about 1" long, many, opposite, small, leathery,   with short petioles and serrated margins; flowers minute, yellowish to reddish; fruit small, capsule surrounded by a disk.   Open places.

T
Conif.
Str. WdL

**108. CASCARA (Rhamnus purshiana).** Small tree or shrub, 6-20' tall, with grayish bark; leaves elliptic to oblong or obovate, 2-6" long,  heart-shaped or obtuse at base, pointed at the tip, <u>veins especially conspicuous beneath,</u> minutely irregularly toothed on the margins; flowers small and greenish, produced in axillary clusters; fruit a fleshy black berry, 1/4 to 1/2'' in diameter.  Moist shady woods; from Idaho and Montana north.

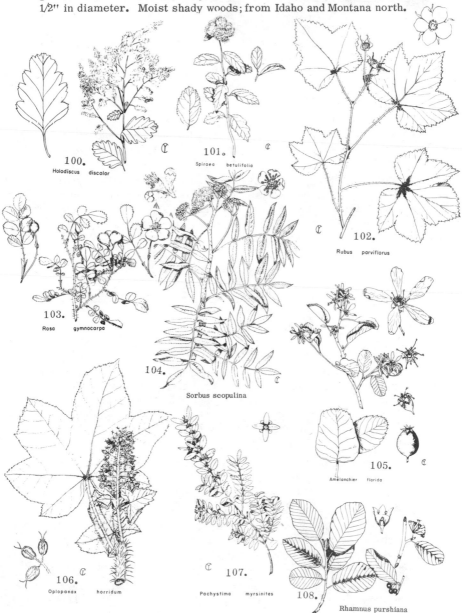

100.
Holodiscus   discolor

101.
Spiraea    betulifolia

102.
Rubus   parviflorus

103.
Rosa     gymnocarpa

104.
Sorbus scopulina

105.
Amelanchier    florida

106.
Oplopanax    horridum

107.
Pachystima    myrsinites

108.
Rhamnus purshiana

T
Conif.
Asp. Wdl.

109. SNOWBRUSH (Ceanothus velutinus). Shrub 2-10' tall; leaves 2-3" long, elliptical, evergreen and shiny, thick and leathery, with 3 prominent veins appearing parallel; flowers creamy-white, in oblong umbel-like clusters of panicles; fruits 3-lobed, sticky, about 1/6 inch wide.

CH
Conif.

110. FOOL'S HUCKLEBERRY (Menziesia ferruginea). Tall slender shrub, 1 1/2-6' tall, with erect branches; leaves thin, pale green elliptic to obovate, round to pointed at the apex, margins entire or finely toothed, mostly glabrous, sometimes with a few rusty hairs; flowers with pedicels, copper-colored, 1/4" long, urn-shaped, in clusters on the ends of the branches; fruit an ovoid capsule, about 1/4" in diameter. Poisonous.

TCH
Conif.
Rocks

*111. BEARBERRY (Arctostaphylos uva-ursi). Plant prostrate and woody; stems 12" or less tall; leaves thick, leathery, spatulate and evergreen; flowers pinkish, urn-shaped, few in a raceme; fruit a red globose berry with bony seeds. Dry places. Edible in jelly or cider.

CH
Conif.
Str. Wd.

*112. MOUNTAIN HUCKLEBERRY (Vaccinium membranaceum). 3-6' tall shrub; leaves coarse, oval or ovate, acute at the tip, finely toothed on the margins, 1/2-1 1/2" long, thin, glabrous; flowers urn-shaped, greenish to pink in color; berries purplish to blue-black, up to 1/2" in diameter, very juicy and delicious when ripe.

TC
Conif.

113. UTAH HONEYSUCKLE (Lonicera utahensis). Erect branching shrub, 1 1/2-4' tall; leaves opposite ovate to elliptical, pale green, thin, 1-2 1/2" long, margins entire, the tips rounded, slightly hairy on the under surface; flowers trumpet-shaped, creamy-white, 1/2-3/4" long, borne in pairs at the tip of the peduncle; berries bright red, in unequal pairs, united at the base, strongly divergent, inedible. Open woods & rocky hills.

GRASSES AND HERBS

TC
Conif.
Meadow
Rocks

114. ONION GRASS (Melica bulbosa). Medium sized bunch grass with enlarged bulb-like base, stems 1-3' tall; leaf blades flat to inrolled, hairless, roughened, or hairy; sheath rough or hairless; panicle narrow, 4-6" long, pale-yellowish, densely flowered, the branches very short; spikelets 3-9 flowered, papery. Open woods, rocky hills, meadows; good forage.

TC
Conif.

115. RATTLESNAKE PLANTAIN (Goodyera oblongifolia). Stem stout, 8-16" tall from a creeping rootstock; leaves nearly all basal, evergreen mottled with white; flowers white to greenish in a one-sided spike-like raceme; upper sepal united with petals to form a hood; lip sac-like, reflexed at the tip; fruit an ovoid to elliptic capsule. Dry or moist areas.

TCH
Conif.
Sub-Alp.

116. YELLOW LAMB'S TONGUE (Erythronium grandiflorum). Stem erect, 6-16" tall, from a narrow deep-seated corm; leaves 2 bright green, appearing basal; flowers large bright-yellow with purple anthers; fruit a a 3-angled capsule. Moist mountain slopes and yellow pine woods.

TC
Conif.

117. WOOD LILY (Trillium ovatum). Stem 8-12" tall; leaves sessile in a whorl of 3 at the summit of the stem; flower petioled, solitary, white changing to pink with age; anthers yellow; fruit a fleshy capsule.

118.  ONE-FLOWERED CLINTONIA (<u>Clintonia</u> <u>uniflora</u>).  Stem slender, 3-5" tall, shorter than the 2-3 basal leaves, usually bearing a single terminal bell-shaped white flower; fruit a blue berry.  Ida. to Mont. & N.

C<br>Conif.

109.  C
Ceanothus     velutinus

110.
Menziesia     ferruginea

111.
Arctostaphylos   uva-ursi

112.
Vaccinium   membranaceum

115.
Goodyera oblongifolia

113.
Lonicera
utahensis

114.
Melica    bulbosa

116.         C
Erythronium   grandiflorum

117.
Trillium     ovatum

118.
Clintonia uniflora

TC
Conif.
Str. Wd.

**119. FAIRY SLIPPER (Calypso bulbosa).** Stem 3-8" tall with sheathing scales; producing 1 basal conspicuously veined foliage leaf, 1-2" long; flower showy, terminal, light rose; the lower petal forms a lip which is 1" long at maturity. Damp mossy coniferous forests.

CH
Conif.
Meadow

**120. SPRING BEAUTY (Claytonia lanceolata).** Perennial rising from a globose corm; stems 2-4" tall; leaves 1 pair, 1-2" long, borne below the inflorescence, lance-shaped; flowers 3-12, pinkish, in a short raceme; fruit a capsule; seeds shiny black. Open woods and meadows.

TC
Conif.

**121. WESTERN BANEBERRY (Actaea arguta).** Stem 1-3' tall; leaves all borne well above the ground; leaflets coarsely toothed or lobed; flowers cream colored, borne in a dense terminal raceme; sepals white or pink-tipped; berry usually bright red; reported poisonous. Moist woods.

CH
Conif.
Meadow
Sub-Alp.

**122. BLUE COLUMBINE (Aquilegia coerulea).** Stem 1-2' tall, glabrous below to glandular pubescent above; leaves compound, mostly from the base, long-petioled and glaucous beneath; leaflets deeply 2-3 cleft, the lobes rounded; flowers usually 1-3, erect, large, deep blue or paler, often white, the spurs long and straight or spreading; follicles about 1" long.

TCH
Conif.
Str. Wd.
Meadow
Sub-Alp.

**123. COLUMBINE (Aquilegia formosa).** Stem 1-3' tall; leaves compound, leaflets shallowly notched, margins with rounded teeth; the flowers few, bright scarlet with yellow petal blades; fruit of several erect follicles about 1" long. Var. flavescens has all yellow flowers and shorter spurs.

TC
Conif.
Meadow
Asp. Wdl.

**124. MEADOW-RUE (Thalictrum occidentale).** Stem slender, 1-3' tall; leaves 3 times compound; leaflets numerous, thin, 3-lobed and roundish at apex; staminate and pistillate flowers on different plants: the staminate flowers greenish with purple anthers; pistils 6-12 with reddish styles; fruit an achene turning backward at maturity. Thickets, woods, meadows.

TC
Conif.
Rocks
Grass

**125. MINTLEAF BEEBALM (Monarda fistulosa var. menthaefolia).** Stems square, 1-2 1/2' tall, growing in dense clumps; leaves opposite, 1-2" long, finely minutely hairy, lance-shaped to ovate lance-shaped, toothed on the margins; petioles very short; flowers purple to rose-colored, 1" long, showy, in a dense terminal head-like cluster; stamens conspicuously exserted; fruit of 4 small nutlets. Strong mint-like odor.

TC
Conif.
Meadow

**126. WOOD VIOLET (Viola glabella).** Stems erect, 3-12" tall from a horizontal rootstock; leaves ovate, 1-3" broad, heart-shaped, sharp at the tip, margins with rounded teeth; lower leaves broadly kidney-shaped on long petioles; flowers bright yellow, 1/2-3/4" wide, with purple veins at the base of the lower petals, spur short. Moist woods and meadows.

T
Conif.
Meadow
Str. Wd.

**127. FIREWEED (Epilobium augustifolium).** Tall perennial with erect stems, 2-5' tall, minutely hairy above; leaves numerous, almost sessile, long lance-shaped, green above, pale beneath, nearly entire; flowers are rose-purple, 1" across, borne in terminal spikes; fruit a long linear, capsule. Widespread, often covering moist burnt-over and disturbed areas.

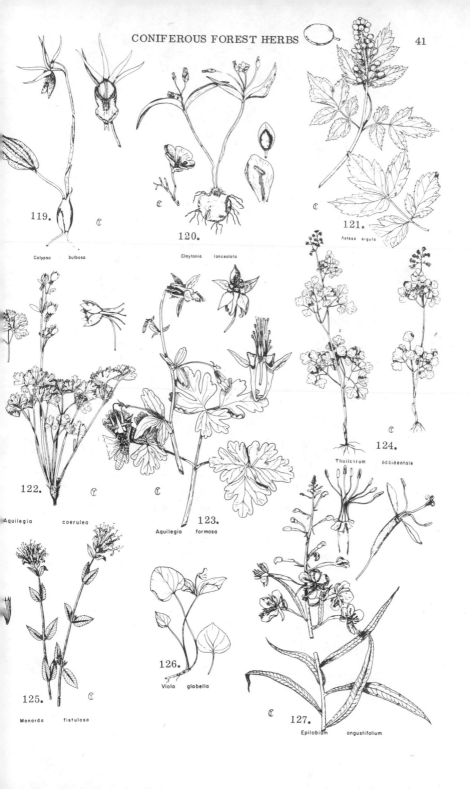

119.

Calypso    bulbosa

120.

121.

Astens   argula

122.

Aquilegia    coerulea

123.

Aquilegia    formosa

124.

Thalictrum    occidentale

125.

Monarda    fistulosa

126.

Viola    glabella

127.

Epilobium    angustifolium

TC
Conif.

**128.  COOLWORT (Tiarella unifoliata).** Stems 1 to several,   10-20"
tall; basal leaves 3-5 lobed, heart-shaped, toothed, sparsely hairy, long
petioled; stem leaves few, short petioled; flowers small, white, borne in
a narrow elongated panicle; fruit a capsule with unequal parts. Moist shady
woods.  Alaska to western Montana and Oregon.

TC
Conif.

**129.  WILD SARSAPARILLA (Aralia nudicaulis).** Glabrous perennial;
stem 1-2' tall; leaf compound, arising from the rootstock;  leaflets 3-5,
oval to ovate, 2-4" long, finely toothed, exceeding the inflorescence; flowers small, greenish, numerous, usually borne in 3 umbels, on a naked peduncle; fruit a purplish-black juicy berry, inedible.  Open woods, brush.

C
Conif.
Marsh

**130.  BUNCHBERRY (Cornus canadensis).** Perennial herb, 4-8" tall,
from a woody underground stem; leaves 4-6 in a whorl at summit of  the
stem; actual flowers minute, greenish, borne in a head surrounded by conspicuous white bracts; fruit globose, bright red.  Coniferous woods, bogs.

TC
Conif.

**131.  PRINCE'S PINE (Chimaphila umbellata).**  Stem usually simple,
6-10"; tall; leaves whorled, leathery-evergreen, short-petioled, elliptic to
oblanceolate, sharply toothed toward the apex; flowers pink, showy, about
1/2" wide, 4-8 in a terminal corymb; fruit a 5-lobed capsule.

TC
Conif.
Meadow
Marsh
Str. Wd.
Sage

**132.  BIRDSBILL (Dodecatheon pauciflorum).**  Glabrous  perennial;
stem 4-16" tall; leaves inverted lance-shaped, 1-4" long,  pale  green,
margins entire or sometimes slightly toothed, rounded at the apex; flowers
3-10, rose-pink to purple, the filament tube yellow; fruit a capsule, 1/2-1"
long at maturity.  Moist woods, bogs and meadows.

T
Conif.
Asp. Wdl.
Sage
Meadow

**133.  CAT'S BREECHES (Hydrophyllum capitatum).**   Stems erect,
short, 4-8" tall, finely hairy, branching from the base; leaves pinnately 5-
7 lobed, 2-4" long, long petioled; calyx rough-hairy; flowers purplish-blue
and bell-shaped, in dense head-like clusters, 1 to several on short peduncles; fruit a capsule.  Woods, banks and rock slides.

T
Conif.
Meadow
Str. Wd.

**134.  INDIAN PAINT-BRUSH (Castilleja miniata).** Stems erect,  1-3'
tall, leaves alternate, lance-shaped to linear, not hairy, margins entire;
flowers tubular greenish, actually quite inconspicuous, the bracts of the
inflorescence scarlet-tipped and very showy.  Moist meadows, woods, etc.

CH
Conif.

**135.  TWINFLOWER (Linnaea borealis var. americana).** Slender trailing evergreen plants forming mats, leaves oval or obovate, leathery, opposite, margins notched at the top; flowers pink or white, 1/2" long, bell-
shaped, in pairs on erect stalks; ovary inferior, densely hairy; fruit a 1-
seeded capsule.  Coniferous woods and banks.

TCH
Conif.
Str. Wd.
Sage

**136.  SCOTCH BLUEBELLS (Campanula rotundifolia).** Stems slender,
5-20" tall, glabrous, often branching from the ground; basal leaves broadly rounded, heart-shaped, 1/4-1" long, toothed or entire,  often withered
and missing at flowering time, stem leaves alternate, narrow, sometimes
linear, about 1-3" long; flowers bluish-purple, 1/2-1" long, bell-shaped,
nodding, one to several, or many in a raceme; fruit a pendulous capsule.

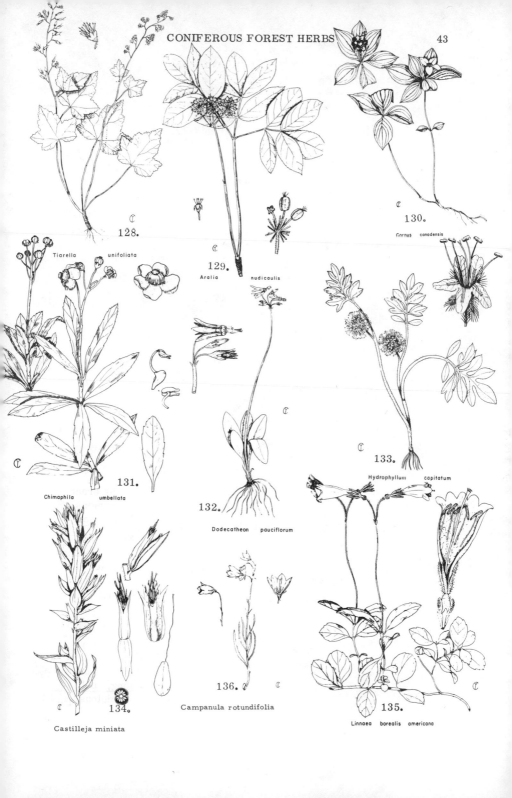

128.

Tiarella unifoliata

129.

Aralia nudicaulis

130.

Cornus canadensis

131.

Chimaphila umbellata

132.

Dodecatheon pauciflorum

133.

Hydrophyllum capitatum

134.

Castilleja miniata

136.

Campanula rotundifolia

135.

Linnaea borealis americana

T
Conif.
Asp. Wdl.
Str. Wdl.
Sage

**137. SHOWY FLEABANE (Erigeron speciosus).** Stems clustered, 4-16" tall, very leafy, glabrous or nearly so; stem leaves ovate, oblong to lance-shaped, glabrous except on midvein and margins; disk flowers yellow, rays 100 or more, bluish, very narrow; fruit a 2-4 nerved achene.

TCH
Conif.
Rocks
Sub-Alp.

**138. PEARLY EVERLASTING (Anaphalis margaritacea).** A white woolly plant with slender stems, 6-24" tall; leaves narrow, 2-4" long, tapering and clasping; flowers appear white, as the central yellow flowers are surrounded by overlapping white papery bracts; inflorescence of compact heads arranged in a compound corymb. Hillsides, woods, rocks.

TC
Conif.

**139. HEART-LEAVED ARNICA (Arnica cordifolia).** Stems 8-20" tall, usually simple or clustered from the base, glandular hairy or villous; basal leaves broadly heart-shaped, long petioled, the margins unevenly toothed; stem leaves 2-4 pairs, smaller, sessile or the lower with short petioles; flower heads large, solitary, or several loosely cymose, rays bright yellow, disks darker; achenes somewhat uniformly hairy.

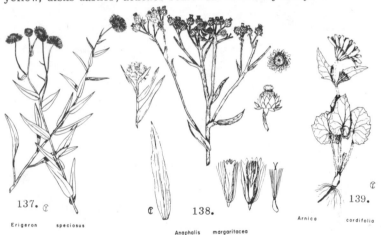

137.    Erigeron    speciosus

138.    Anaphalis    margaritacea

139.    Arnica    cordifolia

OTHER PLANTS FOUND IN THE CONIFEROUS FORESTS:

Trees: 140, white bark pine; 69, blue spruce; 66, quaking aspen.

Shrubs: 45, mountain alder; 46, Rocky Mountain maple; 65, mountain mahogany; 74, wild cherry; 73, choke cherry; 76, Canada buffaloberry; 77, red-osier dogwood; 78, blue elderberry; 79, black elderberry; 80, black twinberry; 65, mountain mahogany; 141, dwarf juniper; 159, shrubby cinquefoil.

Grasses: 16, tufted hair grass; 18, June grass; 21, California wild oatgrass; 23, Sandberg's bluegrass; 24, Kentucky bluegrass; 25, annual bluegrass; 27, tall mannagrass; 29, bluebunch fescue; 30, California bromegrass; 31, downy bromegrass; 34, bluebunch wheatgrass; 35, western rye grass; 38, squirreltail grass.

Herbs: 42, Nelson's larkspur; 43, northern bedstraw; 43, monkshood; 57, blue flax; 58, small-flowered lupine; 61, foxfire; 82, purple clematis; 84, sticky geranium; 143, bear grass.

## SUB-ALPINE PLANTS

This community is limited to the higher slopes of mountains and it is usually confined to a fairly narrow belt of vegetation. The topography is often marked by the occurrence of steep granite cliffs and dry rocky slopes which are described under "Rocks, Cliffs and Slides". The features include the upper part of the coniferous forest dominated by Engelmann Spruce, Alpine Fir and scrubby Whitebark Pine which extends upward to timberline. The area is particularly characterized by the presence of many bogs and mountain meadows which have a very colorful floral display. Here are found some of our most interesting areas for photography.

140. WHITE BARK PINE (Pinus albicaulis). Small alpine tree, 20-30' tall, rarely 60'; trunk normally 2-4' in diameter; branches stout, almost erect, forming an open, irregular broad crown; bark broken by narrow crevices into pale brownish or whitish scales; needles 1 1/2-2 1/2" long, stout, dark green, somewhat incurved, clustered at the ends of branches and borne 5 in a bundle; cones 1 1/2-3" long, ovoid to oval, with broad and thickened scales, remaining closed at maturity. Often gnarled by wind.

*H Sub-Alp. Conif.*

*141. DWARF JUNIPER (Juniperus communis). A low prostrate or creeping shrub, rarely up to 3' tall, forming dense mats covering several feet in area; leaves 1/2-3/4" long, oval shaped, spreading, spine-tipped (not scale-like) in whorls of 3, twisted at the base, dark green with a broad white median line; berries ovoid, 1/4" in diameter, persistent, dark blue, with a whitish cast, edible when ground up and baked with other food.

*H&A Sub-Alp. Conif. Str. Wd.*

142. ALPINE TIMOTHY (Phleum alpinum). Perennial with erect stem 8-20" tall from a decumbent somewhat creeping base; panicle spike-like, oblong, 1/2-2" long, 1/4-1/2" wide; glumes bristly, with awns 1/8" long. Wet places in high mts. Relished by stock for forage.

*AHC Sub-Alp. Meadow*

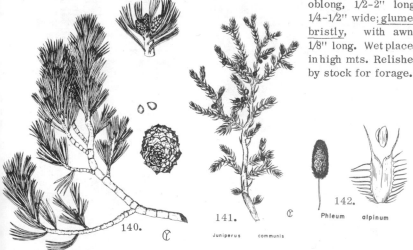

140.
Pinus    albicaulis

141.
Juniperus    communis

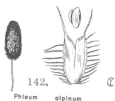

142.
Phleum    alpinum

CH
Sub-Alp.
Conif.

**143. BEAR GRASS (Xerophyllum tenax).** Stem 2-6' tall; leaves stiff and linear forming dense basal tufts; flowers white or cream borne in a dense pyramidal raceme; fruit a capsule. Open woods and slopes.

H
Sub-Alp.

**144. MOUNTAIN DEATH CAMAS (Zygadenus elegans).** Stem 8-40" tall from a deep coated bulb; leaves grass-like, mostly from the base; flowers creamy-white in loose racemes; fruit a 3-lobed capsule. Moist meadows and wet grassy slopes in the mountains. Very poisonous.

H
Sub-Alp.
Meadow

**145. GREEN FALSE HELLEBORE (Veratrum viride).** Stem 2-5' tall; leaves large coarse-veined, corrugated; flowers very numerous, bright or yellowish-green, borne in a loose drooping panicle, fruit a nearly 1" capsule. Moist meadows and hillsides.

HA
Sub-Alp.
Alpine

**146. ALPINE ONION (Allium schoenophrasum).** Stem 8-24" tall; leaves usually 2, cylindrical, hollow, mostly shorter than the stem; flowers pink or white, numerous in a rather compact globose umbel; stamens shorter than the petals; fruit a 3-lobed capsule. Wet meadows and rocks.

TCH
Sub-Alp.
Str. Wd.
Sage
Rocks

**147. SULPHUR FLOWER (Eriogonum umbellatum).** Stem 6-8" tall from an ascending woody base; leaves spatulate 1/2-1" long, densely white woolly beneath, green above; flowers deep sulphur yellow, numerous, borne in a head-like, 3-10 rayed umbel; bracts in a leafy whorl beneath the flower cluster; fruit a 3-angled achene at maturity. Dry hillsides and rocks.

CH
Sub-Alp.
Marsh
Meadow
Sage

**148. WESTERN BISTORT (Polygonum bistortoides).** Perennial with simple, erect stem, 1-2' tall; leaves mostly basal, 6-10" long, including the petiole; stem leaves reduced upward; flowers white in dense spikes, 1-1 1/2" long; fruit a shiny brown, 3-angled achene. Wet meadows, bogs.

H
Sub-Alp.
Rocks

**149. WESTERN WIND-FLOWER (Anemone occidentalis).** Plants at first low, about 4", later the stems up to 20" tall; leaves are silky-hairy, twice-lobed and finely divided; flowers 1-1 1/2" wide, showy, and bluish tinged at the base with conspicuous yellow stamens in the center; sepals 6-8, petal-like; fruit an achene with long silky-feathery tails, these forming a grayish compact globose head. Gravelly slopes and meadows.

CH
Sub-Alp.

**150. ST. JOHNS WORT (Hypericum formosum var. scouleri).** Stems 6-18" tall, simple or branched above; leaves sessile, opposite, oblong to ovate and entire, about 3/4" long, often with translucent spots; flowers are bright yellow, 1/2-3/4" wide, borne in cymose clusters, the closed buds all tinged with dark orange; sepals obtuse; frequently black-dotted; fruit a 3-lobed capsule. Alpine meadows, moist slopes and mountain sides.

H
Sub-Alp.

**151. RED HEATHER (Phyllodoce empetriformis).** A low spreading or erect evergreen shrub with stems 4-18" tall; leaves dark green, needle-like, about 1/2" long, nearly sessile; flowers reddish-pink, small bell-like and about 1/4" long, borne on slender pedicels in clusters at the ends of the branches; fruit a nearly globose capsule. Meadows and rocky slopes.

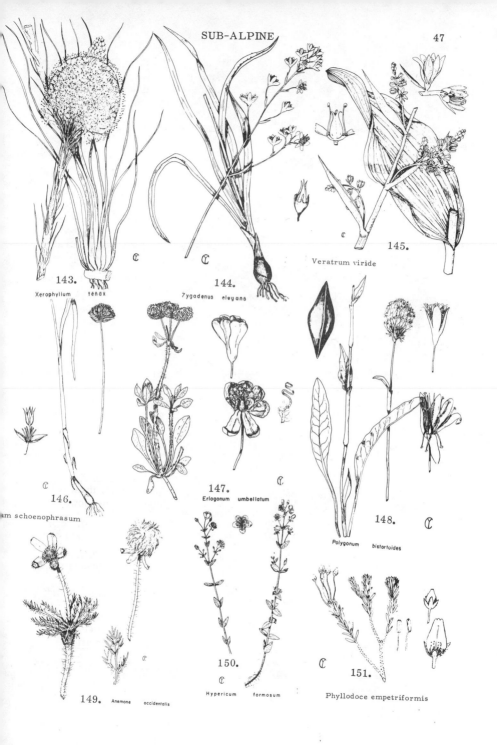

**143.**
Xerophyllum tenax

**144.**
Zygadenus elegans

**145.**
Veratrum viride

**146.**
um schoenophrasum

**147.**
Eriogonum umbellatum

**148.**
Polygonum bistortoides

**149.** Anemone occidentalis

**150.**
Hypericum formosum

**151.**
Phyllodoce empetriformis

CH
Sub-Alp.
Meadow
Str. Wdl.

152. LEWIS' MONKEYFLOWER (Mimulus lewisii). Stems sticky-hairy, clustered, 1-2' tall; leaves opposite, 1-2" long, sharply distantly toothed on the margins; flowers rose-red (rarely yellow or white), large, showy, tubular, about 1" wide and 2" long; fruit a capsule. Wet meadows.

H
Sub-Alp.
Str. Wd.

153. PINK ELEPHANT HEADS (Pedicularis groenlandica). Stems erect, 6-16" tall, often clustered; leaves 2-4" long, finely divided and cut almost to the midrib; flowers reddish-pink, in dense narrow spikes; the elongated beak suggests a trunk and the two lower lobes the ears of an elephant. Moist alpine meadows and streamsides.

TCH
Sub-Alp.
Str. Wd.
Meadow
Rocks

154. MOUNTAIN VALERIAN (Valeriana sitchensis). Stems 1 1/2-3' tall, erect, glabrous except at nodes; basal leaves simple or compound (if so, with 3-7 leaflets), blades ovate or elliptic; stem leaves somewhat narrower and more strongly toothed; flowers white or pinkish, funnel-shaped, borne in a close terminal cluster or head. Alaska to Mont., Ida., Ore.

HA
Sub-Alp.
Meadow

155. MOUNTAIN DAISY (Erigeron peregrinus). Stems 1/2-2' tall; lower leaves oblanceolate, toothed; stem leaves lance-shaped, oval or ovate; heads solitary, 1 1/4-1 3/4" wide; the bracts that surround the head below are spreading, linear, slightly sticky hairy; ray flowers 50-70, pink to purplish colored. Mountain meadows and slopes.

COMMON PLANTS FOUND HERE DESCRIBED IN OTHER HABITATS: Trees and shrubs: 92, Engelmann spruce; 94, alpine fir; 7, bog birch. Grasses and herbs: 38, squirreltail grass; 17, spike trisetum;   44, yarrow; 48, tall white bog orchid; 123, columbine; 138, pearly everlasting; 116, yellow lamb's tongue.


ALPINE

Alpine plants which occur in the high mountains above 10,000   feet must be able to adjust to the rigorous and unfavorable conditions   which exist during the short growing season. It is here that many showy annual and perennial flowers, which are related to arctic vegetation appear growing on gravelly or rocky summits.

HA
Alpine
Rocks

156. MOUNTAIN SORREL (Oxyria digyna). Glabrous perennials; stems 3-12" tall, several from the base; leaves basal, round-reniform on long petioles, 2-5" long; flowers greenish-yellow to reddish, numerous, borne in dense clusters; achenes rose-colored, notched at both ends.

HA
Alpine
Rocks

157. MOUNTAIN DRYADS (Dryas octopetala). Low creeping shrub forming dense mats; leaves oval or oblong, 1/3-1" long, thick, rounded to heart-shaped at the base, dark green and glabrous above, velvety white with a prominent mid-vein beneath, margins inrolled with rounded teeth; flowers white, 3/4-1" wide, terminal on the ends of the naked stems; calyx black-hairy; fruit a cluster of achenes, each tipped with feathery tail.

158. ALPINE JACOB'S LADDER (Polemonium viscosum). Stems clustered at the base, 2-10" tall, whole plant sticky-glandular-hairy; leaves compound, mostly basal; leaflets numerous (25-40) appearing as in whorls, rarely in pairs; flowers pale purple to violet, or rarely yellow, 1/3-3/4" across, broadly bell-shaped with flaring lobes; anthers yellow, not exserted beyond petals; fruit a small capsule. Open rocky slopes high in mts.

HA
Alpine
Rocks

OTHER PLANTS FOUND HERE INCLUDE: most of the herbs that are described in the Sub-alpine section.

152.
Mimulus    lewisii

153.
Pedicularis    groenlandica

154.
Valeriana    sitchensis

155.
Erigeron    peregrinus

156.
Oxyria    digyna

157.
Dryas    octopetala

158.
Polemonium    viscosum

Rocks, boulders, cliffs and rock slides are common in all mountainous terrain making excellent hiding places for the rodents, birds, reptiles and amphibians which live here. Also, certain plants are adapted to cliffs and rocks growing under very dry conditions or in the spray of adjoining waterfalls or wet seepage slopes from springs. Many live on rocky slides (talus slopes). However, there are few species entirely limited to this habitat.

159. SHRUBBY CINQUEFOIL (Potentilla fruticosa). Low or medium sized shrub, 1-4' tall, with dense leafy branches: leaves pinnately compound; leaflets 3-7, narrowly lance-shaped or oblong, 1/2-3/4" long, silk-hairy on both surfaces; flowers golden yellow, 1/2 - 1" wide, borne in cymes or solitary, near the ends of the branches; achenes covered with whitish hairs. Moist rocky outcrops, woods and meadows.

TC
Str. Wd.
Asp. Wdl.
Conif.
Meadow
Sage
Rocks

159.
ℂ

Potentilla          fruticosa

PLANTS OCCURRING HERE DESCRIBED
IN OTHER HABITATS:
Shrubs: 71, white-stemmed gooseberry;
79, black elderberry; 98, swamp currant;
111, bearberry.
Grasses:29, blue-bunch fescue; 114, onion grass; 38, squirreltail grass.
Herbs: 88, spear-head ragwort; 125,
mint-leaf bee-balm; 138, pearly everlasting;
147, sulphur flower; 149, western windflower; 154, mountain valerian; 156, mountain sorrel; 157, mountain dryads; 158, alpine Jacob's ladder.

# COMMON MAMMALS

All of the mammal species described in this guide are almost entirely covered by a dense coat of fur. Mammals are further characterized by bearing their young alive and nursing them on milk until they can feed themselves.

Because of their nocturnal activities and secretive habits, most mammals, especially the smaller kinds, are not well known to the general public. Nevertheless, they exhibit the highest type of intelligent behavior found in the animal kingdom and posses interesting and instructive habits. The diurnal species may be located and easily studied in their natural habitat, particularly in our great national parks. The nocturnal varieties, especially the small rodents and shrews, may be captured in live traps and observed while in captivity. In the field of nature photography, mammals are fine subjects.

Most of the mammals you will meet are described in this guide. The chart shown here illustrates the comparative sizes of four well-known species of mammals. These sizes are mentioned after most of the mammals described in the text. Unless

MOUSE 3 - 4"

RAT 8 - 11"

CAT 15 - 18"

RACCOON 2 - 3'

otherwise indicated, the figures following the scientific names in the species account are those of body length followed by tail length.

Review the body shapes and color patterns given in the species accounts and illustrations. Check carefully the range and habitat of each species against the locality and habitat where you are observing. Look carefully at the pictures of the different groups of mammals, such as mice, rabbits, weasels, and so forth, until you thoroughly learn the characteristic appearance of these and other groups of mammals.

1.    2.

## SHREWS

CH
Water

1. **WATER SHREW** (Sorex palustris). 3-4"; mouse size. Upper parts dark grayish or blackish, frosted with whitish hairs; under parts grayish-white to grayish. Tail dark above, white below; stiff hairs along outer side of foot; fur of soft velvety texture; easily distinguished by color pattern from other shrews and by pointed snout from any mouse. Expert swimmer.

TC
Marsh
Meadow
Rocks
Str. Wd.
Conif.

2. **WANDERING SHREW** (Sorex vagrans). 2 1/2"; 1 3/4"; mouse -. Reddish-brown above, grayish-brown below; dark brown in winter. Third unicuspid tooth in upper jaw smaller than fourth. Like a small mouse, but with more slender body and long pointed nose; eyes and ears very small. Forages in leaf mold under shade during day, or in weeds, brush or bogs.

CHA
Alpine
Conif.
Rocks
Sub-Alp.

3. **CINEREOUS SHREW** (Sorex cinereus). 2 1/2"; 1 1/2"; mouse -. Pale brown above, slightly darker on rump; grayish-white below. Darker and more grayish in winter; distinguished from other shrews by pale brown color, smaller size, and third upper unicuspid tooth same size or larger than fourth. Usually found north of Canadian border in heavy moist forest.

CHA
Sub-Alp.
Conif.
Rocks

4. **DUSKY SHREW** (Sorex obscurus). 2 1/2"; 2"; mouse -. Dark brownish-red above, pale brownish-gray below; slightly grayer in winter. Third upper unicuspid tooth smaller than fourth. Similar to Wandering Shrew, but has longer tail. Wooded and moist habitats; commoner in north.

## BATS

TCH
Air

5. **LITTLE BROWN BAT** (Myotis lucifugus). Length 3 1/3"; forearm 1 1/2"; mouse -. Color variable, yellowish to brown to almost black. Fur tips on back bronzy, imparting glossy sheen to pelage. Ears short, not extending past nose when laid forward. Often forms large colonies in attics of houses; common in clearings.

5.

TCH
Air

6. **YUMA BAT** (Myotis yumanensis). Length 3"; forearm 1 1/3"; mouse -. Dull brownish in color; fur woolly. A similar bat to above, but does not have glossy tips to hairs. Common.

TCH
Air
Conif.

7. **LONG-EARED BAT** (Myotis evotis). Length 3 1/4"; forearm 1 1/2"; mouse -. Color greenish-yellow to dull brownish-yellow. Distinctive long black ears, which, when laid forward, extend more than 3/16" beyond nose.

TCH
Air

8. **LONG-LEGGED BAT** (Myotis volans). Length 3 3/4"; forearm 1 1/2"; mouse -. Dark brown to blackish; largest of the Myotis bats. Ears short, rounded; under side of wing furred out to elbow. Late and slow flying.

TC
Air

9. **SMALL-FOOTED BAT** (Myotis subulatus). Length 3"; forearm 1 1/4"; mouse -. Body orange or yellow in color; face and ears black; fur long and silky; size of body and feet small. Dry fields, but often near water.

10.  BIG BROWN BAT (Eptesicus fuscus). Length 4 1/4"; forearm 1 7/8"; mouse size.  Distinguished from similar bats by large size,  rich brownish-red color, and small black ears.  Common in lower mountain forests. TC Air

11.  SILVER-HAIRED BAT (Lasionycteris noctivagans).  Length 3 3/4"; forearm 1 2/3"; mouse size.  Dark dusky brown in color, with hairs on back tipped with white, giving frosted appearance; tail membrane furred. TCH Air

12.  HOARY BAT (Lasiurus cinereus). Length 5"; forearm 2 1/4"; mouse size.  Large bat, with wingspread about 16".  Body brownish in color with whitish wash; ears small and black-rimmed; tail membrane furred above. High rapid flyer, but usually flies later at night than other bats. TCH Air

## RABBIT-LIKE ANIMALS

13.  CONY (Ochotona princeps).  7 1/2", rat size.  Brownish or yellowish in color.  Usually seen sitting hunched up on top of a boulder in mountain rock slides.  High-pitched eek or enk call distinctive.  Ears short and rounded; feet furred on soles; hard to see because of resembling rocks. HA Rocks

14.  WHITE-TAILED JACKRABBIT (Lepus townsendi).  20"; 3 1/4"; cat size.  Largest rabbit in region.  In summer, grayish, finely mixed with black and brown above, white below.  In winter, pure white.  Tail white with faint black band on top.  Distinguished by long ears and hind legs.  Active at all times except midday when it rests under bush.  Uncommon. TCH Grass

15.  SNOWSHOE HARE (Lepus americanus).  16"; 2"; cat size.  Brownish hare with dark brown head and light brown rump and sides; under parts and legs dirty white.  In winter, pure white with blackish-brown edgings on ears, and with large pads of stiff thickly-packed hairs on soles of hind feet. Nocturnal, but often seen foraging at edge of clearings at dawn and dusk. TCH Conif. Sub-Alp.

16.  BLACK-TAILED JACKRABBIT (Lepus californicus).  20; 4"; cat size.  Iron-gray or brownish-gray upper parts; grayish-white below.  Ears large, black-tipped; separated from White-tailed Jack by tail which is solid black on top.  Occasionally bounds high in spy leap.  Mainly in s. half region. T Sage

15. Snowshoe Hare

14. White-tailed Jackrabbit

15.            14.

13. Cony

17. Mountain Cottontail

19. Yellow-bellied Marmot      22. Columbian Ground Squirrel

**17. MOUNTAIN COTTONTAIL (Sylvilagus nuttallii).** 13; 1 1/2"; cat ‑.
T
Sage
Str. Wd.
Marsh
Pale brownish-gray, with gray sides and rump; under parts white; pale buffy-brown on legs; bright yellow-brown patch on nape of neck and upper shoulders; tail appears solid white "cotton tail" (which is best field mark).

**18. PYGMY RABBIT (Sylvilagus idahoensis).** 11"; 3/4"; cat ‑. Body
T
Sage
grayish, tinged with pinkish; under parts lighter; has no "cotton tail". Small size, relatively short ears and legs distinctive. Seldom seen till it is flushed, then runs quickly into brush. Found in south half of our region.

## MARMOTS

**19. YELLOW-BELLIED MARMOT (Marmota flaviventris).** 16"; 7";cat
TCH
Rocks
Grass
Sub-Alp.
size. Like a large heavily-bodied ground squirrel. Grizzled yellowish-brown above; head dark, with a white bar on the nose. Under parts yellow or rich reddish-brown; sides of neck yellow; feet yellow to brown and tail dark brown. Common in rocks; hibernates in winter; aestivates in hot days.

**20. HOARY MARMOT (Marmota caligata).** 20"; 9"; cat +. Large gray-
HA
Rocks
Sub-Alp.
Alpine
Meadow
ish marmot of the sub-alpine rocks. Head black with white facial markings; body grayish, becoming lighter on shoulders; feet black; tail is dark brownish. Grayish color, habitat, and shrill piercing whistle distinctive.

21. WOODCHUCK (<u>Marmota</u> <u>monax</u>). 20"; 5"; cat size. Small dark marmot of shy habits. Cinnamon brown above, frosted with white-tipped hairs; reddish-brown below; tail brownish; head mostly unmarked. <u>Separated from other marmots by even dark colors, unmarked head, and small size</u>. Lives in rocks or burrows in earth; diurnal. Extreme north of region.

H
Sub-Alp.

## GROUND SQUIRRELS AND CHIPMUNKS

22. COLUMBIAN GROUND SQUIRREL (<u>Citellus</u> <u>columbianus</u>). 12"; 4 1/2"; rat+. <u>Upper parts mottled grayish, washed with yellowish or brownish and weakly spotted with yellowish</u>; sides of neck yellow; nose and face yellow to light brown; feet yellowish-brown; under parts buffy to light brownish. Tail long and bushy; largest ground squirrel in our area; hibernates in hole. High-pitched alarm note. Lives in northern part of region.

TCH
Meadow
Grass
Rocks
Sub-Alp.

23. RICHARDSON'S GROUND SQUIRREL (<u>Citellus</u> <u>richardsoni</u>). 8 1/2"; 3 1/2"; rat size. Upper parts whitish, washed with yellow or orange; under parts pale yellow to whitish; tail dark above, light red below; <u>plain yellow color pattern identifies</u>. Stiff upright posture; hibernates. N. and e. of region.

TC
Grass
Meadow
Sub-Alp.

24. UINTA GROUND SQUIRREL (<u>Citellus</u> <u>armatus</u>). 9"; 3"; rat size. Upper parts brownish-gray with faint grayish head and shoulders; under parts buffy white; tail black mixed with white. Separated from other plain backed ground squirrels by <u>general grayish color</u>. Prefers moist meadows and brush by water; dormant late summer to spring. E. Ida., w. Wyo., sw. Mont.

TCH
Grass
Marsh
Meadow
Sub-Alp.

25. GOLDEN-MANTLED GROUND SQUIRREL (<u>Citellus</u> <u>lateralis</u>). 8"; 4 1/2"; rat size. <u>White stripe, bordered by two black stripes, on each side</u> of back; back brownish-gray; sides buffy; belly whitish to buffy; <u>head and shoulders rich hazel brown;</u> narrow white line above and below eye; black and white stripes on sides and general chipmunk-like habits identify this species. Prefers rocky places in forests, but also open pine woods.

TCH
Rocks
Sub-Alp.
Conif.

26. IDAHO GROUND SQUIRREL (<u>Citellus</u> <u>brunneus</u>). 7 1/2"; 2 1/2"; rat -. Small brownish-gray ground squirrel with <u>distinct grayish-white spots on back;</u> sides and under parts grayish; tail brownish-black. Small size and spots on back distinctive. West central Idaho valleys and clearings.

TC
Meadow

25. Golden-mantled Ground Squirrel    27. Northwestern Chipmunk

TCH
Conif.
Sub.-Alp.
Rocks

27. NORTHWESTERN CHIPMUNK (<u>Eutamia</u> <u>amoenus</u>).    5"; 4"; rat -.
<u>Black (or dark brown), and white stripes on back</u>. Sides yellowish or light
brownish; under parts whitish or buffy; tail brownish above, light brownish
or grayish below. Distinctive size and rich colors. Prefers open forests.

TCH
Sage
Conif.
Jun-Mah.

28. LEAST CHIPMUNK (<u>Eutamias</u> <u>minimus</u>). 4"; 3 1/2"; mouse +. General grayish or light-brownish coloration.    <u>Small size and the brownish</u>
<u>dark dorsal stripes distinguish this variable species</u>.    Gray form usually
found in sagebrush, darker form in brush of coniferous forests.

TCH
Conif.
Sub-Alp.
Rocks

29. RED-TAILED CHIPMUNK (<u>Eutamias</u> <u>ruficaudus</u>). 5"; 5 1/4"; rat -.
Large dark-colored chipmunk. Shoulders and sides reddish; dorsal stripes
black and white (mixed with reddish); <u>under side of tail red</u>:  belly  white.
Prefers dense forests of northern Idaho and northwestern Montana.

CH
Conif.
Sub-Alp.

30. UINTA CHIPMUNK (<u>Eutamias</u> <u>umbrinus</u>). 5"; 4"; mouse +.   Large
dark chipmunk with brownish-gray sides, grayish head and rump, and broad
brownish dorsal stripes; belly white.  Extreme e. Ida., w. Wyo., n.e. Utah.

31.  Red Squirrel

34.  Flying Squirrel

35. Northern Pocket Gopher

39.  Western Harvest Mouse

38.  Deer Mouse

## TREE SQUIRRELS

31. RED SQUIRREL (Tamiascurus hudsonicus). 8"; 5"; rat size. Medium-sized tree squirrel with brownish, reddish, or reddish-gray back, a dark brown or black tail, and white belly separated from darker color of back by black stripe. Loud scolding cry. Common in conifers.

TCH
Conif.
Sub-Alp.

32. EASTERN GRAY SQUIRREL (Sciurus griseus). 10"; 9";    rat +. Large size; long bushy tail; gray in color, with yellow tinge; occasional in black phase. Wild in some city parks. 33. EASTERN FOX SQUIRREL (Sciurus niger). 14"; 12"; cat -. Large squirrel; reddish-yellow, becoming more grayish on back and more orange on belly. Wild in or near cities.

Urban

34. FLYING SQUIRREL (Glaucomys sabrinus). 7"; 5 3/4"; rat size. Small squirrel with fur of soft woolly texture, brownish above, dirty white below. Tail fluffy; head with small ears and large black eyes. Nocturnal and seldom seen except on moonlit nights, gliding from tree to tree.

TCH
Conif.
Sub-Alp.

## POCKET GOPHER

35. NORTHERN POCKET GOPHER (Thomomys talpoides). 5 1/2"; 2 1/2". Small rat-sized rodent with brownish fur, blunt head, large yellow exposed teeth, small eyes and short sparsely-haired tail. Claws of fore feet large for digging; forages below ground surface in burrows and seldom seen above ground; pushes up soil in "gopher hills". Often in colonies in soft soil.

TCH
Grass
Meadow
Sub-Alp.

## MICE

36. WESTERN HARVEST MOUSE (Reithrodontomys megalotis). 2 3/4"; 2 3/4"; mouse size. Small slender mouse, brownish-buff above; whitish below; tail slim and thinly haired; long tan-colored hairs inside ears; outer face of upper incisors grooved. In dense grass and weeds, near streams.

T
Grass
Meadow
Sage

37. HOUSE MOUSE (Mus musculus). 3 1/2"; 3". Grayish-brown above, buffy below, with naked tail covered by ring-like scales. Buildings.

38. Western Jumping Mouse

38. DEER MOUSE    (Peromyscus maniculatus). 3 1/2"; 3 1/4"; mouse size. Long-tailed mouse with large ears; grayish or reddish-brown above, white below; Very abundant; bi-colored body distinctive.

TCH
Conif
Rocks
Sage
Jun-Mah.
Str. Wd.
Sub-Alp.

39. WESTERN JUMPING MOUSE (Zapus princeps). 3 3/4 "; 5 3/4"; mouse size. Small fore-feet, large hind feet, and very long tail. Back brownish, sides yellow or orange with intermixed black hairs; belly white; tail bi-colored, dark above, whitish below. Occasionally seen hopping along in dense grass or brush or in forest openings near water.

TCH
Marsh
Meadow
Str. Wd.

40. LONG-TAILED MEADOW MOUSE (<u>Microtus longicaudus</u>). 5"; 2 1/2"; mouse +. This and the following mice are technically known as "voles", characterized by stout body, very short ears, a relatively short tail, and dark brownish or grayish color, the under parts being little lighter than the upper parts. This species is best identified by grayish-brown to grayish color, relatively long tail, and body size; belly lighter gray than in other voles.

TCH
Grass
Meadow
Marsh
Str. Wd.
Sub-Alp.

40. Long-tailed Meadow Mouse

CH
Str. Wd.
Marsh
Water

41. RICHARDSON'S MEADOW MOUSE (<u>Microtus richardsoni</u>). 6"; 3"; rat -. Largest of the voles. Reddish-brown above, grayish below; hair relatively coarse; tail long. Semi-aquatic, preferring vegetation near water.

TC
Grass
Marsh
Meadow

42. MOUNTAIN MEADOW MOUSE (<u>Microtus montanus</u>). 4 1/2"; 1 1/2"; mouse size. Medium-sized vole with brownish to blackish upper parts, gray under parts, and relatively short tail. Dense grass or weeds;s.part region.

CHA
Rocks
Conif.
Meadow
Sub-Alp.
Alpine

43. HEATHER MOUSE (<u>Phenacomys intermedius</u>). 4 1/4"; 1 1/2"; mouse size. Grayish-brown above, grayish-white below, with white feet. Fur long and soft. Angles between cusps on inner side of lower molars twice as deep as those on outer side of jaw. Other voles have inner and outer angles about equal.

CH
Str. Wd.
Marsh

44. NORTHERN BOG LEMMING (<u>Synaptomys borealis</u>). 4"; 5/8"; size of mouse. Small vole with brownish-gray upper parts, grayish under parts, short ears, long thick fur, very short tail (about as long as hind foot), and upper incisors grooved on outer face. Wet meadows and bogs of extreme n.

TCH
Conif.

45. NORTHERN RED-BACKED MOUSE (<u>Clethrionomys gapperi</u>). 4"; 2"; mouse size. Back distinctly reddish, sides grayish; under parts grayish-white. Usually found in dense coniferous forests throughout region.

T
Sage
Grass

46. SAGEBRUSH MOUSE (<u>Lagurus curtatus</u>). 3 3/4"; 5/8"; mouse size. A small light-colored vole with very short tail. Upper parts pale grayish or yellowish-brown; under parts whitish.

### RATS

47. BUSHY-TAILED WOODRAT (<u>Neotoma cinerea</u>). 8 1/2"; 7"; rat size. Brownish-gray upper parts, white feet and tail; bushy tail; large ears and long whiskers. Young "packrats" are bluish-gray. Stealing habits and strong musky

TCH
Rocks
Conif.

47.

odor. Frequents rock slides and old buildings, mostly in forested areas.

48. BROWN RAT (Rattus norvegicus). 7 3/4; 7". This is the only other Urban rat in our area. Brownish above, grayish-white below; tail long and naked.

## BEAVER, MUSKRAT AND PORCUPINE

49. BEAVER (Castor canadensis). 28"; 10"; raccoon size. Largest ro- TCH dent in North America. Large semi-aquatic mammal with coarse reddish Str.Wd. brown hair, small ears and eyes, and typical flattened paddle-shaped tail. Water Marsh Builds dams and mound-shaped lodges; warns by slapping tail on water.

50. MUSKRAT (Ondatra zibethica). 11"; 9 1/2"; rat +. Large semi- aquatic rodent. Fur dense; upper parts rich brown in color, overlaid with TC glossy hairs; under parts silvery. Tail long and rat-like, though flattened Water Marsh sideways, and mostly naked. Lives in or near water; digs burrows in banks and builds mound-like lodges; wanders far from water in spring and fall.

51. PORCUPINE (Erethizon dorsatum). 22"; 8 1/2"; raccoon size. Clumsy heavy- bodied rodent with long black hair (some- times yellow instead of black);back, sides and tail armed with sharp-pointed whitish quills. Often found walking clumsily along trail or perched in tree; feeds on bark.

TCH Conif. Sub-Alp. Jun.-Mah. Sage

51.

49.

50.

## DOG FAMILY

52. COYOTE (Canis latrans). 35"; 15"; raccoon +. Medium- TCHA sized brownish-gray dog with long All heavy fur and slender build. Belly and throat whitish or yellowish; variable. Tail held down between between legs. Yipping bark.

52.

54.

### 53. GRAY WOLF (Canis lupus).

CHA
Conif.
Sub-Alp.

40"; 20"; raccoon +. Looks like large      53.
German Shepherd dog. Colors vari-
able, being grayish, brownish or blackish on back and sides and somewhat
lighter below. Ears short, muzzle heavy; when running, carries tail at an-
gle from body (see illustrations). Utters long drawn-out howl. Wild areas.

### 54. RED FOX (Vulpes fulva).

CH
Sub-Alp.
Conif.
Rocks

30"; 16"; raccoon +. Slender dog-like
mammal with long slim legs and long bushy tail. Colors variable: red phase:
black ears, reddish-yellow body, black legs, red tail with white tip; silver
phase: black with white-tipped guard hairs and black tail with white tip; black
phase: black, except white tip on tail; cross phase: brown with a blackish
"cross" over shoulders. White tip on end of bushy tail distinctive for all.

55.

56.

## BEARS

TCH
Conif.
Sub-Alp.
Meadow
Marsh

55. BLACK BEAR (Ursus americanus). 5-6'; 2-3' at shoulder. Colors variable, ranging from black to brown, cinnamon, or "blond". Tail very
short; pelage relatively long and shaggy; toe nails short and black; no well
developed hump on shoulders; common in forests. Usually shy.

TCH
Conif.
Sub-Alp.
Meadow

56. GRIZZLY BEAR (Ursus arctos). 6-8'; 3-4' at shoulder. A large
heavy-bodied bear, sometimes reaching half a ton in weight. Hair long and
shaggy, giving woolly appearance; color variable, from yellow to brown or
blackish, but hairs usually tipped or "grizzled" with whitish. Obvious hump
on shoulders, heavy large size, and long yellow or brown claws distinctive.
Shy and seldom seen; a few scattered through wilder areas.

57. RACCOON (Procyon lotor). 24"; 12". Medium-sized carnivore with grizzled brownish-gray body, black mask over eyes, and alternating rings of yellowish and black on the long bushy tail. Muzzle sharp-pointed; toes long and "finger-like". Often in trees; nocturnal; common near water. **TCH** Str. Wd. Water Marsh Asp. Wdl. Conif.

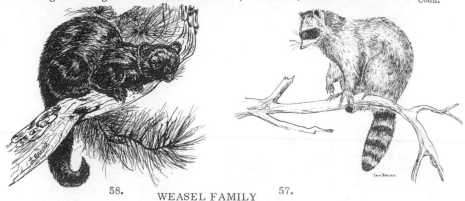

58.                    WEASEL FAMILY          57.

58. FISHER (Martes pennanti). 24"; 14"; raccoon size. Resembles the more common marten in body proportions, but much larger. Brownish-black with white-tipped hairs above, somewhat darker below. Spends much time in trees; very shy, rare and seldom seen. **CH** Conif. Sub-Alp.

59. MARTEN (Martes americana). 15"; 17 1/2"; cat size. Small arboreal weasel-like carnivore, with brownish or reddish-yellow upper parts, and somewhat lighter under parts containing a yellow or orange throat and chest patch; head slightly tinged with grayish. Like mink, but longer pelage has beautiful soft fluffy texture. Commonly chases squirrels in trees. **CH** Conif. Sub-Alp.

60. LONG-TAILED WEASEL (Mustela frenata). 11"; 7"; rat +. Small slender long-bodied carnivore with prominently arched back. In summer, upper parts brownish, under parts yellow or orange; tail brown with black tip. In winter, all white, except black-tipped tail. Commonest in rocks. **TCH** Meadow Grass Rocks Conif. Sub-Alp. Str. Wd.

60.                              59.

63.

62.

64.

65.

66.

67.

TCH
Meadow
Grass
Rocks
Conif.
Sub-Alp.
Str. Wd.

61.  SHORT-TAILED WEASEL (<u>Mustela</u> <u>erminea</u>).  8"; 3 1/2";  rat -.
Similar to Long-tailed Weasel, but pale yellow or white beneath and smaller.

TC
Str. Wd.
Water
Marsh

62.  MINK (<u>Mustela</u> <u>vison</u>).  16"; 8"; cat -.  Large weasel-like carnivore, entirely glossy-brown in color, with irregular patches of white on the
throat.   Tail about 1/2 body length and moderately bushy. Even dark coloration, terrestrial habits, and size are distinctive. Hunts fish in streams.

CH
Conif.
Meadow
Sub-Alp.

63.  WOLVERINE (<u>Gulo</u> <u>luscus</u>).  30"; 8"; raccoon +.  Large size (30
lbs), appearing much like small bear.  Mostly dark brownish  with  <u>broad
yellowish stripe running back on each side from shoulder to rump and then</u>
out on tail; dark under parts broken by white or orange markings on throat;
light patches on head.  A fabled predator of the north, but rare in Rockies.

64. BADGER (Taxidea taxus). 23"; 6"; raccoon size. Distinctive low flattened appearance, short legs and long fur. Upper parts yellowish, mixed with black hairs; under parts pale yellow; pelage noticeably grayer in winter; head with black and white markings. Tail short and bushy; claws of the fore feet long for digging. Digs up rodents from holes in open areas.

TCH
Grass
Meadow
Conif.
Sub-Alp.

65. SPOTTED SKUNK (Spilogale gracilis). 14"; 6"; rat +. Small carnivore with black coat marked with a series of white lines and spots over the head, back, and sides. Tail black with white tip. Feet with long claws. Nocturnal; anal glands discharge a disagreeably smelling fluid when animal is distrubed. Prefers brush, rocks and buildings.

TC
Meadow
Marsh
Str. Wd.
Rocks

66. STRIPED SKUNK (Mephitis mephitis). 18"; 10"; raccoon -. Totally black, except for prominent white stripe passing from back of head along each side of back to base of tail; white striped down middle of face between eyes; tail black with intermixed white hairs. Fur long and silky; fore feet with long claws. Can throw strong smelling oil 10' or more. Nocturnal.

TCH
Conif.
Meadow
Str. Wd.
Rocks

67. RIVER OTTER (Lutra canadensis). 28"; 18"; raccoon +. Large stream-lined weasel-like carnivore, with short legs, webbed feet, thick tapering tail, broad head, prominent whiskers, and short dense fur. Color dark brownish, somewhat lighter below with silvery sheen. Semi-aquatic.

TCH
Water
Marsh

## CATS

68. MOUNTAIN LION (Felis concolor). 60"; 30"; raccoon +. Occasionally weighs up to 180-200 lbs. Fur short; color reddish or grayish; lighter below; tail long, its tip dark brown; back of ears and sides of nose dark. Shy, rarely seen.

TCH
Conif.
Rocks
Jun-Mah.
Sub-Alp.

68.

70.                     69.

CH
Conif.
Sub-Alp.

69. CANADA LYNX (Lynx canadensis). Raccoon +; 36"; 4". Medium-sized bob-tailed cat; upper parts gray with yellowish tinge; the under parts

gray with faint black spots; more reddish in summer.   Large ear tufts; ears edged with black; dark line on back from head to tail; prominent "side burns" of hair on face; legs long and unspotted; feet large; black-tipped tail.

**TCH**
**Conif.**
**Rocks**
**Sub-Alp.**

70.  BOBCAT (Lynx rufus). 28"; 6"; raccoon +. Bob-tailed cat, similar to the Canada Lynx, but smaller, with shorter hair and prominent spotting on body.  Color grayish or reddish above and buffy or whitish below; sides and legs distinctly spotted; ear tufts and "side burns" short.  Feet small; tip of tail black on top and preceded by two black bars; legs slender.

## DEER FAMILY

71.
72.
73.
74.

71.  ELK (Cervus canadensis).

**TCH**
**Meadow**
**Conif.**
**Sub-Alp.**

Height 4 1/2-5'; weight, ♀ 500 lbs; ♂ 800 lbs.  General body color yellowish or reddish-gray; head and neck dark, becoming dark brown in ♂; legs dark reddish-brown; pale yellow rump patch; tail same color. Bulls larger than cows, with long shaggy hair on neck and large antlers; ♀ without antlers.

**TCH**
**Meadow**
**Conif.**
**Marsh**
**Sub-Alp.**

72.  MULE DEER (Odocoileus hemionus).  Height 3-3 1/2'; weight 200-400 lbs.  Large deer with characteristic two-branched tine pattern of antlers and large ears.  Color grayish in winter, buffy in summer; a white patch on throat; rump patch white; tail white with black tip.  Antlers in ♂.

73. WHITE-TAILED DEER (Odocoileus virginianus).  Height 3-3 1/2';  TC
weight, 100-300 lbs.  Antlers form two main beams sweeping backwards and  Conif.
then curving forwards with a series of upward-pointing tines along beams.  Meadow
Tail long and bushy, with white under surface; no white rump patch;  during winter, upper parts grayish-brown, under parts whitish; in summer, upper parts reddish-brown to tan.  When excited, tail carried upright.       TCH
                                                                          Meadow
74. MOOSE (Alces americana).  Height 5-6 1/2'; weight 900-1000 lbs.  A   Str. Wd.
large horse-sized deer with immense palmate antlers in ♂.  Blackish-brown  Marsh
color: pendulous muzzle; "bell" (flap of skin) on throat.  Eats water plants.  Water
                                                                          Sub-Alp.
75. BARREN GROUND CARIBOU (Rangifer arcticus).  Height 3 1/2-4 1/2';      CH
weight 200-600 lbs.  Large flaring antlers and heavy broad hooves.  Body  Sub-Alp.
blackish-brown; grayish-white neck, belly, rump and surface under tail.  N.  Meadow
                                                                          Conif.

PRONGHORN AND BOVINES

79. Bighorn Sheep

77.

78.  Mountain Goat    76.

76. PRONGHORN ANTELOPE (Antilocapra americana).  Height  3';   T
weight 100-125 lbs.  Tan or yellow-colored, with whitish rump, belly, and  Grass
two broad bands across throat; horns distinctive, slightly curved forward.  Sage

77. AMERICAN BUFFALO (Bison bison).  Height 5-6'; weight 800-2200
lbs.  Unique large head, shaggy mane, hump on shoulders, weak hind quar-  TC
ters, short black horns and dark brown color; both sexes with horns.  Once  Grass
widespread in grasslands, but now restricted to parks and preserves.      Meadow

# COMMON BIRDS

Of all animals, birds are perhaps the best known. Their attractive color patterns, beautiful songs, and interesting and purposeful actions make them the most appreciated of living things. Most are active in daylight.

This guide will introduce you to many interesting birds of the Northern Rockies faunal area. Study the illustrations and descriptions in the following pages. Carefully learn the identifying characteristics of the various groups of birds, such as sparrows, owls, woodpeckers, shorebirds and so forth.

The descriptions that follow are necessarily brief, but they call your attention to the most important field marks by which a species may be recognized. Occasionally the song, if distinctive, is described. Particularly note the bird's habitats (shown on side of page) as well as its range in our territory. Be sure to get as good a view as possible of the bird you are studying.

The above chart will help you estimate sizes of birds. The warbler is 4-5" in length; sparrow, 5-6 1/2"; robin, 8-10"; mourning dove, 11-13"; and crow, 18-22". In the following descriptions, each species is compared in size with one of these five birds. A + sign means "larger than", while a - sign means "smaller than". Figures in the descriptions give total lengths. Common species you are likely to meet are now described.

===================================================================
## CONCLUSION OF MAMMAL SECTION

HA
Rocks
Sub-Alp.

78. MOUNTAIN GOAT (Creamnos americanus). Height 3-3 1/2'; weight 150-300 lbs. Large white goat or sheep-like mammal with long shaggy hair. Pelage entirely white, but with black horns and hooves. Lives among cliffs.

HA
Sub-Alp.
Rocks

79. BIGHORN SHEEP (Ovis canadensis). Height 3-3 1/2'; weight 150-275 lbs. Large goat or sheep-like mammal with short close hair and thick curving horns in the ♂. Upper parts brownish or brownish-gray, with white rump patch, lower belly, and tip of muzzle; tail short and dark. Chin without beard. Horns of ♀ short, erect, and slightly back-curved. Horns in both sexes prominently marked with transverse ridges. Expertly climbs rocks.

(Swift divers.)

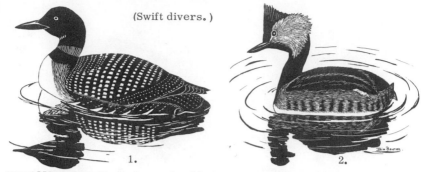

1.

2.

1. COMMON LOON (Gavia immer). 30"; crow +. Large goose-sized water bird with black upper parts, spotted and streaked with white on sides of neck, back and wings; under parts white. Bill heavy, but sharp-pointed, and not at all duck or goose-like. Distinctive drawn-out quavering cry. Prefers lakes, mainly in forested areas; breeds throughout most of region. **TC Water Marsh**

2. EARED GREBE (Podiceps caspicus). 14", crow -. Medium-sized water bird. Head, neck, and breast black, with tuft of long yellow feathers behind each eye along sides of head; rest of upper parts blackish, with reddish-brown sides and silvery white under parts. Feathers on top of head form sharp-pointed crest; bill appears slightly upturned. Breeds in region. **TCH Water Marsh**

3. HORNED GREBE (Podiceps auritus). 14"; crow -. Similar to Eared Grebe, but has reddish neck and throat and conspicuous light-yellow ear tufts on otherwise black head; back and wings black; belly silvery-white. Bill stout, but sharp-pointed; white wing patch shows in flight. Breeds in n. **T Water Marsh**

4. RED-NECKED GREBE (Podiceps grisegena). 20"; crow size. Medium-sized grebe with black crown, grayish cheeks, and red neck; remainder of upper parts brownish; under parts whitish; bill yellowish and about as long as head; two white patches in wing in flight. Distinguished from Horned Grebe by size and gray cheeks. Also nests in north part of region. **T Water Marsh**

5.

5. PIED-BILLED GREBE (Podilymbus podiceps). 14"; crow -. Small grebe with chicken-like bill which is whitish with black band across the middle. Chin and throat black, with rest of upper parts and lower throat brownish; under parts silvery-white, mottled with brownish. Breeds in ponds and marshes. **T Water Marsh**

6. WESTERN GREBE (Aechmophorus occidentalis). 28"; crow +. A large grebe with long, slender, swan-like neck. Top of head, back of neck, and back slaty black; cheek, forepart of neck, throat, and under parts white; bill yellow; white patch on each wing in flight. Breeds mainly on lakes. **T Water Marsh**

## PELICANS

7. WHITE PELICAN (Pelecanus erythrorynchos). 60"; crow +. Very
large white bird with black wing-tips and yellow patch on throat; bill and
feet orange-yellow. Birds fly in high formation; breed on lakes.

T
Water
Marsh

## HERONS AND BITTERNS

8. GREAT BLUE HERON (Ardea herodias). 45"; crow +. Large, long-
necked long-legged wading bird with general bluish-gray coloration; bill
yellow, long, and sharp-pointed. Neck drawn into shoulders in flight; long
black plumes on head. Stands about 4' high. Voice: hoarse croaks.

TCH
Marsh
Water

9. SNOWY EGRET (Leucophoyx thula). 25"; crow +. Medium-sized,
all white heron with black bill and legs and yellow feet. Prominent plumes
in breeding season. Irregular in south in summer by water at low elev.

T
Water
Marsh

10. BLACK-CROWNED NIGHT HERON (Nycticorax nycticorax). 26";
crow size. Chunky short-legged heron with white forehead, cheeks, throat,
and belly; blackish crown and back; neck and sides grayish; bill black; two
long white plumes on head. Breeds near water in lowlands.

T
Water
Marsh

11. AMERICAN BITTERN (Botaurus lentiginosus). 30"; crow +. A
large-sized rich golden-brown marsh bird with strongly-streaked plumage.
Crown, sides of neck and wing tips dark; throat white; bill yellow; legs are
greenish. Often seen with long neck up-stretched, looking like surrounding
cattails. "Umph-ka-choonk" note distinctive. Breeds in low marshes.

## SWANS, GEESE AND DUCKS

12. WHISTLING SWAN (Olor columbianus). 52"; crow +. Very large
all white water bird with long graceful neck; bill and feet black; young birds
are grayish brown; some adults water-stained brownish or yellowish. Migrant and winter resident on large bodies of water; most numerous in winter from northern Wyoming and southern Idaho southward.

TCH
Marsh
Water

12A. TRUMPETER SWAN (Olor buccinator). 65"; crow +. Very similar to above, but larger. Breeds and winters mainly around Yellowstone.

T
Water

13. CANADA GOOSE (Branta canadensis). 40"; crow +. Large goose-
like water bird with long neck and webbed feet; head and neck black with
white chin and cheek patches; back, wings, and upper sides brownish-gray.
Tail white near base; belly whitish or grayish; bill and feet black; honking
call and V-formation in flight distinctive. Breeds and visits along rivers.

T
Water
Marsh

14. SNOW GOOSE (Chen hyperborea). 30"; crow +. A medium-sized
goose, all white, except black wing tips; bill red (edges black); feet dark
red; sub-adults dusky-mottled on head and neck. Migrant around water.
15. ROSS'S GOOSE (Chen rossii). 22"; crow size. Bill lacks black edges.

TCH
Water

16. MALLARD (Anas platyrhynchos). 26"; crow +. Large duck with
dark green head, grayish body, dark ruddy breast, and white collar and tail;

TC
Water
Marsh

bill yellow; feet orange; blue patch on wing; under surface of wings whitish
in flight. ♀ brownish, mottled with dark. Loud "quack"  of ♀ and weak
"yeeb-yeeb-yeeb" of ♂ typical.

T
Water
Marsh

17. GADWALL (Anas strepera). 20"; crow size. Overall grayish coloration on upper parts, white belly and patch on hind edge of wing, and black
and brown tail are distinctive. ♀ similar to ♂, but browner. Resident.

T
Marsh
Water

18. PINTAIL (Anas acuta). 28"; crow +. Large duck with long slim
neck and long pointed tail. Head and upper neck dark, separated on sides
by white stripe running along neck; rest of upper parts grayish; breast and
belly white; long black tail feathers; ♀ brownish. Breeds and migrates.

T
Marsh
Water

19. CINNAMON TEAL (Anas cyanoptera). 16"; crow -. Body cinnamon red with large blue patches on fore edges of wings. ♀ brownish with
reddish tinge. Breeds and migrates at low elevations of our region.

T
Marsh
Water

20. AMERICAN WIDGEON (Mareca americana). 20", crow size. Medium-sized duck with conspicuous white crown. Rest of body brownish with
gray head (greenish patch below eye) and white patch on fore edge of wing.
♀ brownish with gray head. Breeds and migrates throughout region.

T
Marsh
Water

21. SHOVELER (Spatula clypeata). 20"; crow size. Large bill, black
head and back, white breast, reddish sides, and blue wing patches distinctive. ♀ brownish with blue wing patches. Breeds and migrates in region.

22.  GREEN-WINGED TEAL (Anas carolinensis).  15" crow -.  Small
duck with grayish body, white mark in front of wing, brown head with green    T
patch back of eye, bright green patch on wing, and white belly; pale yellow   Marsh
patch underneath on each side; bill black; feet brownish.  ♀ speckled brown-  Water
ish, with bright green patch on wings.  Fast direct flight.  All year resident.

23.  BLUE-WINGED TEAL (Anas discors).  16"; crow -.  Small dull-
colored brownish duck with large white crescent in front of  eye  and large   T
light blue patch on fore edge of wing.  ♀ mottled brownish, without facial     Marsh
crescent, but with blue patch on wing; bill black; feet yellowish.  Summer.    Water

24.  LESSER SCAUP (Aythya affinis).  16"; crow -.  Medium-sized duck
with blue bill and black head, neck, breast, back (mottled with white), and    T
tail.  Flanks and lower belly grayish-white.  ♀ brownish, with white spot in   Marsh
front of eye; white stripe in outer half of wing.  Scattered breeder & migrant. Water

25.  REDHEAD (Aythya americana).  20"; crow size.  Head and upper
neck reddish; lower neck, breast and tail black.  Rest of upper parts gray-    T
ish; belly white; head rounded with high abrupt forehead and bluish bill.  ♀  Marsh
grayish-brown.  Breeder and migrant throughout region.                         Water

26.  RING-NECKED DUCK (Aythya collaris).  18"; crow size.  Like the
Lesser Scaup, but with black back and head, bluish bill crossed at base and    T
near tip with white rings and tipped with black; white of side running up into Marsh
black of back in front of wing.  ♀ brownish with pied bill and white eye-ring. Water
Scattered breeder.

27.  CANVASBACK (Aythya valisineria).  24"; crow +.  Large grayish-
white duck with black breast and tail, brownish-red neck and head, and long    T
black bill.  Flat forehead slopes in line with upper outline of bill.  ♀ more  Marsh
grayish.  Breeder, migrant and winter visitor.                                 Water

28.  BUFFLEHEAD (Bucephala albeola).  15"; crow -.  Small mostly-
white duck; part of head in front of eyes, lower cheeks, chin, nape, and back  TC
black.  Upper cheeks, crown and rest of under parts white; wing black with     Marsh
large white patch.  ♀ dusky with white cheek spots.  Breeds n., migrates s.    Water

29.  BARROW'S   GOLDENEYE
(Bucephala islandica).  22"; crow +. A
large sized black and white appearing
duck with black head showing   white      CH
crescent-shaped patch in front of eye.     Marsh
Upper parts black mottled with white,      Water
the black of the back coming almost to
the water line in front of wings; neck,
breast and under parts white.  ♀ grayish with white color & dark brown head.

29.

30.  COMMON GOLDENEYE (Bucephala clangula).  22"; crow +.  Large   TCH
chunky duck with dark head, back and tail, and black and white wings.  Rest   Marsh
                                                                               Water

of body white; <u>round white spot between eye and bill;</u> black of wings not touching water line. ♀ very similar to that of Barrow's Goldeneye. Breeds in northern part of territory, rare winter visitor elsewhere.

TC
Conif.
Marsh
Water

31. WOOD DUCK (<u>Aix sponsa</u>). 18"; crow -. <u>Small beautifully-colored duck,</u> with white chin, <u>vertical white streaks on cheeks, and vertical black and white streaks in front of wing;</u> drooping crest; In summer ♂ similar to ♀, but with red and white bill. ♀ duller, with white eye-ring, white chin and black bill. Breeds near forest lakes and ponds.

T
Marsh
Water

32. RUDDY DUCK (<u>Oxyura jamaicensis</u>). 15"; crow -. <u>Small, chunky, neck-less duck with fan-shaped wren-like tail.</u> Rusty red in color with a black crown, white cheeks, blue bill, grayish belly. ♀ duller. Scattered.

33.                              34.

CH
Water
Str. Wd.

33. HARLEQUIN DUCK (<u>Histrionicus histrionicus</u>). 16"; crow -. Small bluish-black duck with <u>reddish sides and numerous white marks on head,</u> neck, and shoulders. ♀ dark, with 3 white spots on cheeks. Spring, summer.

TC
Water

34. AMERICAN MERGANSER (<u>Mergus merganser</u>). 26"; crow +. Large <u>mostly black and white appearing duck with long thin reddish bill;</u> head and middle of back black; lower back and tail gray; rest of body whitish. ♀ is grayish with red head and bill and white wing patch. Uncommon.

TC
Conif.
Water

35. HOODED MERGANSER (<u>Lophodytes cucullatus</u>). 18"; crow size. Small black and white duck with brownish flanks and <u>large fan-shaped white crest, narrowly bordered with black on head.</u> ♀ brownish with white patch on wing. Breeds on ponds and small lakes in wooded areas.

## VULTURES, HAWKS AND EAGLES

TCH
Rocks
Air

36. TURKEY VULTURE (<u>Cathartes aura</u>). 30"; wingspread 5' or more; crow +. Large, eagle-sized bird, <u>wholly black in color with lighter under surface of wings and naked red head.</u> Soars high in air on motionless slightly up-tilted wings, rocking unsteadily from side to side. Summer, open.

TCH
Conif.
Asp. Wdl.
Sub-Alp.

37. GOSHAWK (<u>Accipiter gentilis</u>). 25"; crow +. Large hawk with short rounded wings and long rounded tail; back dark bluish-gray; under parts of body light marbled gray; white line over eye; top of head blackish. Res.

40.

36.

38.

37

38. SHARP-SHINNED HAWK (Accipiter striatus). 14"; crow -. Small bluish-gray hawk with short rounded wings and long square-tipped tail. Under parts white, streaked or barred with reddish. In flying, alternates several quick wing-beats with a glide. Resident and migrant; hunts birds.

TCH
Conif.
Sub-Alp.

39. COOPER'S HAWK (Accipiter cooperii). 18"; crow size. Small bluish-gray hawk with short rounded wings and long rounded tail. Reddish- or black-streaked white below. Accipiter hawks fiercely ambush birds in woods.

Conif.
Str. Wd.
Jun-Mah.

40. RED-TAILED HAWK (Buteo jamaicensis). 19-24"; crow +. Large broad-winged fan-tailed hawk with dark brown upper parts, lighter under parts, and a red tail. Immature similar, but has dark gray tail, barred with black, and dark mid-belly area. Some individuals dark all over, except for red tail. Distinctive gull-like screaming "pee-er", descending in pitch. Does much soaring, hunting mainly mammals. Common resident.

TCH
Conif.
Rocks
Sage
Air

41. ROUGH-LEGGED HAWK (Buteo lagopus). 20-24"; crow +. Broad-winged long-tailed hawk with black back, top of tail, and (usually) a black belly. Head and breast buffy, streaked with blackish; under surface of tail whitish; feathery pantaloons on legs buffy, streaked with black; black patch at "wrist" on under surface of wing. Winter resident in our region.

T
Sage
Grass
Rocks

42. FERRUGINOUS HAWK (Buteo regalis). 24"; crow +. Large broad-winged hawk, reddish-brown above and whitish below, with light reddish streaks on head; tail grayish-white; in flight, shows 2 light-colored areas on upper surface of wings; feathers on legs dark. Dark phase with light tail.

T
Sage
Grass
Rocks

43.

44.

45.

46.

47.

52.

TH
Sage
Grass
Rocks

    43. SWAINSON'S HAWK (<u>Buteo</u> <u>swainsoni</u>). 20-22"; crow size. Broad-winged hawk similar in size to the Red-tailed Hawk, but with longer more pointed wings. <u>Broad dark breast band is distinctive; forward half of under</u> <u>surface of wing is light colored (buffy) and unmarked, contrasting with dark</u> <u>back half of wing</u>; tail grayish below; upper parts immaculately dark colored. Dark individuals are best told by under-wing pattern. Summer.

TCH
Grass
Sage
Sub-Alp.
Air

    44. GOLDEN EAGLE (<u>Aquila</u> <u>chrysaetos</u>). 30-40"; crow +. Immense size (wingspread up to 7 1/2'). Brownish-black in color, with golden-brown crown and hind neck. Legs feathered to toes; tail slightly or strongly barred.

TC
Near
Water
Air

    44A. BALD EAGLE (<u>Haliaetus</u> <u>leucocephalus</u>). 30"; crow +. <u>Very large</u> <u>and black with white head and tail</u>; feet yellow, unfeathered. Lakes & rivers.

45. MARSH HAWK (Circus cyaneus). 19-24"; crow size. Large hawk with long blunt black-tipped wings and a long rounded tail. Color uniformly grayish in ♂ or dark brownish in♀, with a white rump. In flying, wings are held arched above the horizontal. Resident and migrant in open areas. `TCH Meadow Grass Sub-Alp. Marsh`

46. OSPREY (Pandion haliaetus). 21-25"; crow +. A large hawk with long pointed wings and short rounded tail. Blackish upper parts and white under parts. Often seen hovering over water, or plunging in feet first for fish. Circles high in air, often giving rising series of shrill whistles. Summer resident and migrant along lakes and large rivers. `TCH Water Sub-Alp. Air`

47. SPARROW HAWK (Falco sparverius). 9-12"; robin +. Small hawk with long pointed wings and long square-tipped tail. Wings bluish-gray; back reddish, barred with black; tail reddish with black bar near tip; under parts light; face strongly marked with black (including falcon "mustaches") and white. Flies direct like falcon; often hovers. Summer, migr., winters s. `TCH Grass Meadow Sage Sub-Alp.`

48. GYRFALCON (Falco rusticolus). 20-24"; crow +. Large falcon. Top of head heavily streaked with white; upper parts grayish to grayish-brown, mottled with dark grayish; under parts white, spotted on belly and flanks with blackish-brown. Falcon facial marks faint. Rare winter visitor. `TCH Meadow Sub-Alp.`

49. PRAIRIE FALCON (Falco mexicanus). 17"; crow size. A large long-winged falcon with light brown to grayish upper parts, dark brown mustaches, pale brown tail, and whitish under parts, which are immaculate on throat, but streaked on breast and belly. Swift flier in dry open areas. `TH Meadow Sage Grass`

50. PEREGRINE FALCON (Falco peregrinus). 16-20"; crow size. A large falcon with typical quick deep wing beat, long pointed wings, and long narrow tail. Dark bluish-black above; buffy white below, marked with fine spots and barrings; black mustache marks under eyes. Scattered in region. `TCH Grass Meadow Water`

51. PIGEON HAWK (Falco columbarius). 10-14"; robin +. Small falcon with long pointed wings and long square-tipped tail. Back dark bluish-gray; tail heavily barred; under parts buffy, streaked with brownish; faint falcon facial markings. Summer resident and migrant in north. `TCH Conif. Sub-Alp.`

### GROUSE

52. BLUE GROUSE (Dendragapus obscurus). 17-23"; crow size. Dark grayish above, finely mottled with blackish; tail dark brownish-gray; under parts grayish; throat, sides, and flanks are all streaked with whitish; feathers bordering neck sacks white; a yellow-orange patch over eye. ♀ like ♂ but browner. Voice of 5-6 low booming hoots. `TCH Conif. Sub-Alp.`

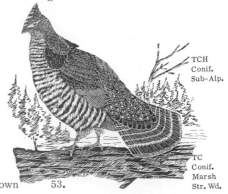

53. RUFFED GROUSE (Bonasa umbellus). 16-19"; crow size. Reddish-brown `TC Conif. Marsh Str. Wd.`

53.

small-chicken-size bird <u>with black band at end of tail.</u> Grayish or reddish-brown in color, finely blotched and streaked with dark; prominent tufts of feathers on sides of neck. Produces accelerating drum-roll sound with the wings. Common dense mixed or deciduous woodlands.

CH
Conif.
Sub-Alp.

54. SPRUCE GROUSE (<u>Canachites</u> <u>canadensis</u>). 16"; crow -. Upper parts dark brownish, marked with black; <u>lower back and tail coverts barred</u> <u>with black and white</u>; tail black; small orange-red patch over eye; under parts black, barred with white on sides and belly. ♀ brownish. Conifers.

58.

55.

HA
Sub-Alp.
Alpine
Rocks
Meadow

55. WHITE-TAILED PTARMIGAN (<u>Lagopus leucurus</u>). 12-13"; robin +. Small grouse of the open alpine areas of the mts. <u>Brownish with white</u> <u>belly, wings and tail in summer</u>. Wholly white, except for black eyes and bill, in winter. Usually found above timber line on the higher mountains.

T
Grass
Sage

56. SHARP-TAILED GROUSE (<u>Pediocetes</u> <u>phasianellus</u>). 17"; crow size. <u>Sharp-pointed tail distinctive.</u> Upper parts pale brownish, speck-led with blackish; throat buffy; under parts whitish, marked on breast and sides with dark brown spots. Occurs in open dry areas at low elevations.

TCH
Sage

57. SAGE HEN (<u>Centrocercus</u> <u>urophasianus</u>). ♂ 28"; ♀ 22"; crow +. A large grouse, <u>grayish-buff in color, and finely marked with darker bars</u> <u>and spots</u>; more white on head, neck and sides; belly black. Tail feathers long and stiff, held in fan-shape by ♂ at mating time.

62.

63.

## QUAIL, PARTRIDGES AND PHEASANT

58. CALIFORNIA QUAIL (Lophortyx californicus). 9-11"; robin +. A grayish-brown quail with a short plume curving forward over face from the crown; plume shorter in ♀. Throat black in ♂; light brown in ♀. Back brownish-gray; tail gray. Loud "kuk-wher-go" call distinctive. Valleys.

T
Meadow
Grass
Marsh

59. MOUNTAIN QUAIL (Oreortyx pictus). 11"; robin +. Somewhat similar to California Quail, but characterized by long straight backward-pointing plume on the head and bright brownish-red throat. Call a loud "too-look". Found in arid areas of western mountains of our region.

T
Meadow
Rocks

60. HUNGARIAN PARTRIDGE (Perdix perdix). 11-13"; dove size. A large quail with reddish-brown head, brownish back, gray breast, and dirty-white belly separated from the breast by a broad sooty-brown bar; tail is reddish in flight. Open areas and fields at low to moderate elevations.

T
Meadow
Grass

61. CHUKAR PARTRIDGE (Alectoris graeca). 13". Large grouse with brownish-gray upper parts, gray forehead, black line through eye, white throat (bordered by black line), gray breast, reddish belly, & barred sides.

TCH
Rocks
Sub-Alp.
Sage

62. RING-NECKED PHEASANT (Phasianus colchicus). ♂33-36"; ♀ 20-24"; crow +. A large long-tailed chicken-like bird. ♂ is highly colored with white collar and long sweeping tail. ♀ smaller, brown and grouse-like. Crow of ♂ a double-noted "cu-cuck". Common in agricultural areas.

T
Meadow
Rocks
Marsh

## CRANES AND COOT

63. SANDHILL CRANE (Grus canadensis). 34-46"; crow +. Large gray heron-like bird with a bald red forehead. Unlike heron, the crane flies with its head and neck outstretched (not folded back). Migrant; breeds in s.

TCH
Meadow
Marsh

64. WHOOPING CRANE (Grus americanus). 50"; crow +. Large white heron-like bird, white except for red face and black wing tips. Rare migrant.

TCH
Meadow

65. COOT (Fulica americana). 13-16"; crow -. Duck-sized blackish-gray bird with a black head and neck and a white bill. Moves head back and forth while swimming; conspicuous long legs and unwebbed but frilled feet.

.T
Marsh
Water

65. SHORE-BIRDS 66.

66. KILLDEER (Charadrius vociferus). 10-11"; robin size. The familiar robin-sized plover of shores, meadows, golf courses and fields. Two

T
Marsh
Meadow

black bands across throat and light red tail; head black and white; back grayish-brown; under parts mostly white; common in open areas.

H
Marsh
Meadow

67. MOUNTAIN PLOVER (Eupoda montana). 8-10"; robin size. Small shorebird with light grayish-brown upper parts and whitish under parts; white forehead and line over eye, with black bar between bill and eye and front part of crown; white stripe in wing. Breeds in east part of region.

68.                                              70.

TC
Meadow
Marsh

68. COMMON SNIPE (Capella gallinago). 10-11"; robin+. Upper parts brownish, heavily striped and barred with black; throat and breast buffy, streaked with brown; belly white; bill long; no large white stripe on back.

TCH
Meadow
Marsh

69. SHORT-BILLED DOWITCHER (Limnodromus griseus). 11-12"; robin +. Long-billed brownish snipe-like bird with white lower back and rump; under parts light reddish-brown; white stripe down middle of back distinctive in flight. Migrant throughout our region.

TCH
Marsh
Water

70. SPOTTED SANDPIPER (Actitis macularia). 7-8"; robin -. Upper parts dark grayish; lower parts white, covered with large round black spots. Fall plumage similar, but without spots. Constant teetering while on ground and bowed stiffly-held wings in flight are distinctive. Migrant and regular summer resident along rivers, streams and mountain lakes.

80.                          75.

71. UPLAND PLOVER (Bartramia longicauda). 11-12"; robin +. Medium-sized buff-brown shorebird, heavily streaked with darker brown. A long neck and tail; belly whitish; bill relatively short. Holds wings elevated for a moment upon alighting. Prefers arid grasslands.

*TCH Meadow Marsh Grass*

72. SOLITARY SANDPIPER (Tringa solitaria). 7-9"; robin -. Dark-colored sandpiper with white belly; legs dark greenish; best field marks are white tail strongly barred with black plus white eye-ring. Migrant & summer resident, mostly seen along edges of ponds and streams.

*TCH Marsh Water*

73. LEAST SANDPIPER (Erolia minutilla). 5-6"; sparrow size. Small sparrow-sized sandpiper, brown and black-streaked above, whitish below; breast is grayish, spotted with dark brown; characterized by yellow-green legs and black bill. Migrant along shores and boggy flats.

*T Marsh Shores*

74. SEMIPALMATED SANDPIPER (Ereunetes pusillus). 6"; sparrow size. A small "peep", very similar to the Least Sandpiper in fall, from which it may be separated by black instead of yellow legs, stouter bill, grayer color, and relatively unspeckled breast. White of sides comes up in front of the bend of the wing (unlike in Least Sandpiper). Migrant.

*T Marsh Shores*

75. LONG-BILLED CURLEW (Numenius americanus). 24"; crow size. Large, almost chicken-sized, brownish shorebird with a long down-curved bill, averaging 5-7" long. Note: loud harsh "cur-lee". Breeds in arid hills.

*TCH Meadow Grass*

76. WILLET (Catoptrophorus semipalmatus). 15-17"; crow -. Large gray and white shorebird with a relatively short straight stout bill and bluish legs. Uniform mottled grayish color when at rest and flashing black and white wing pattern in flight are distinctive. South part of our region.

*T Grass Marsh*

77. GREATER YELLOWLEGS (Totanus melanoleucus). 12-15"; dove size. Large gray and white shorebird with long bright yellow legs and a slightly upturned black bill. Shows dark wings and white rump and tail in flight. Spring and early fall migrant.

*TH Meadow Marsh Shores*

78. LESSER YELLOWLEGS (Totanus flavipes). 9-11"; robin +. Identical in color to Greater Yellowlegs, but bill shorter and perfectly straight; body also smaller and less bulky. Migrant throughout our region.

*TH Meadow Marsh Shores*

79. MARBLED GODWIT (Limosa fedoa). 18"; crow -. Large shorebird with a long straight or slightly upturned bill and uniform buffy brown coloration marked with blackish-brown spots and bars. Uncommon migrant.

*T Shores*

80. AMERICAN AVOCET (Recurvirostra americana). 18-20"; crow size. Large shorebird with a very long thin upturned bill and striking black and white coloration. Head and neck pinkish in breeding season; bill black; feet blue. Breeds on small ponds and lakes in open arid places.

*TC Meadow Marsh Water*

81. WILSON'S PHALAROPE (Steganopus tricolor). (Picture on next page.) 9-10"; robin size. Spring ♀ characterized by broad red collar, broken on nape, and dusky-gray shoulder and upper part of head; throat white; wings and back dark grayish, blotched with red; upper breast grayish and

*T Water Marsh*

82.

81.

83.          87.

rest of under parts white; bill black; legs greenish. ♂ similar, but duller; upper parts dark brown, spotted with grayish; under parts whitish, faintly washed on neck and upper breast with pale reddish. Breeds on ponds.

## GULLS AND TERNS

TCH
Water
Marsh

82. CALIFORNIA GULL (Larus californicus). 20-23"; crow +. Medium-sized greenish-footed gull with a light gray mantle (wings and upper middle of back). Wing tips black, marked with white; bill yellow with red or red and black spot on lower mandible. Breeds on large lakes.

T
Water
Marsh

83. RING-BILLED GULL (Larus delawarensis). 18-20"; crow size. Similar to California Gull, but slightly smaller and has yellow or yellow-green feet and a yellow bill crossed by black band near tip. Sub-adults have conspicuous black band in otherwise white tail. Common; breeding on lakes.

T
Water

84. HERRING GULL (Larus argentatus). 22-26"; crow +. Large pink-footed gull with a light gray mantle. Wing tips black, marked with white; bill yellow with red spot on lower mandible. Irregular migrant.

T
Marsh
Water
Fields

85. FRANKLIN'S GULL (Larus pipixcan). 14-15"; crow -. A small gray-backed gull, with a black head, white under parts (pale rosy breast), dark red bill and feet, black wing tips (margined at feather tips with white) separated from gray of mid-wing by a white band, and (in winter) a white head with a dark patch extending around the nape from eye to eye. Lakes.

86. BONAPARTE'S GULL (Larus philadelphia). 12-14"; dove size. A small, red-footed gull, with outer half of wing white, edged with black. Head black in summer, but in winter white with a black spot behind eye; bill black. Migrant in region, particularly in late summer and early fall.   T Water

87. FORSTER'S TERN (Sterna forsteri). 14-15"; dove +. Like a small graceful gull, white in color, with a light grayish mantle, black cap, reddish bill (black tip) and feet, and deeply forked tail; wing primaries lighter than, or as light as, rest of wing; rump grayish. In fall, dark patch on head extends as band from eye to ear only. Breeds on lakes in open areas.   T Marsh Water

88. COMMON TERN (Sterna hirundo). 13-16"; dove +. Similar to Forster's Tern, but with wing primaries darker than rest of wing; whitish rump; dark head patch in fall extending completely around back part of head.   T Marsh Water

89. CASPIAN TERN (Hydroprogne caspia). 21"; crow size. Large gull-sized tern with black top of head, grayish upper parts and white under parts. Forehead black, streaked with white in winter; bill large and red; under surface of wing tips shows considerable black. Irregular breeder on lakes.   T Marsh Water

90. BLACK TERN (Chlidonias nigra). 9-10"; robin size. Graceful little tern with short slightly-forked tail. In spring, black head and upper parts, dark gray back and wings, and white under surface of tail. Lighter in fall and winter, with head (except for dark markings around eye, ear and nape) and under parts whitish, and wings and back dark gray. Summer.   T Marsh Water

91.          DOVES          93.

91. MOURNING DOVE (Zenaidura macroura). 11-13". Small, slender brownish dove with a pointed tapering tail. Notes of slow mournful "coo-ah-oo, coo, cook, coo" distinctive. Breeds in open dry areas.   TC Woods Brush

92. ROCK DOVE (Columba livia). 14"; dove +. The domestic pigeon. Color variable, usually with much blue, gray or white. Common resident in urban and farm areas; also found wild in dry rocky canyons.   T Bldgs. Rocks

OWLS

93. SCREECH OWL (Otus asio). 8-10"; robin +. Small owl with conspicuous ear tufts. Plumage intricately marked with spots and bars, but   TC Conif. Str. Wd. Asp. Wd.

giving a general brownish or grayish appearance.     Under parts lacking conspicuous stripes.   Notes: tremulous "oo͵ oo, ͵oo-oo-oo-oo", gaining in tempo toward the end;   only tremolo heard at distance.  Common resident.

96.

99.

*Short-eared Owl*

94.  FLAMMULATED OWL (<u>Otus</u> <u>flammeolus</u>).  7"; sparrow +.   <u>Very small owl, mostly grayish, with brownish tinge</u>; brownish eyes,  unfeathered feet, and very small ear tufts.   Scattered resident in mt. forests.

C
Conif.
Asp. Wdl.

95.  BARN OWL (<u>Tyto</u> <u>alba</u>).  14-19"; crow -.   Medium-sized long-legged earless owl with buffy and grayish upper parts and buffy-white  under parts.   <u>Heart-shaped monkey-like face and light coloration are distinctive.</u>  Uncommon local resident, mostly in agricultural areas and buildings.

T
Barns
Fields

96.  HORNED OWL (<u>Bubo</u> <u>virginianus</u>).  18-25"; crow +.   <u>Large brownish or brownish-gray owl</u>, heavily marked below with cross-wise barrings.  <u>Large ear tufts or "horns arise from sides of head.</u>.   Notes: a solemn deep-toned series of 4-8 hoots given in definite rhythmical cadence.    ♂: "hoo-hoo, hoo, hoo" or "whoo-hoo-hoo, hoo, hoo".   ♀: "Whoo-hoo-hoo, hoo-hoo, hoo"; higher pitched and more rapid than ♂'s.  Common resident.

TCH
Conif.
Str. Wd.
Asp. Wdl.
Sub-Alp.

97.  LONG-EARED OWL (<u>Asio</u> <u>otus</u>).  13-16"; crow -.   <u>Medium-sized owl with long ear tufts or "horns" arising near center of head.</u>   Buffy to grayish, marked with lengthwise streaking; face reddish.   Summer resident.

TC
Conif.
Str. Wd.

98.  SNOWY OWL (<u>Nyctea</u> <u>scandiaca</u>).  20-26"; crow +.   <u>Large  white owl</u>, heavily marked with narrow blackish cross-wise bars.  Winter visitor.

T
Fields

99.  SHORT-EARED OWL (<u>Asio</u> <u>flammeus</u>).  13-17"; crow -.   <u>Medium-sized owl; buffy in color, heavily streaked with dusky.</u>   Resembles a hawk when flying, but flies more slowly and appears big-headed; often seen  in daytime.   Resident, preferring swamps, marshes, meadows and fields.

T
Grass
Meadow
Marsh

100.  HAWK OWL (<u>Surnia</u> <u>ululu</u>).  15-17"; dove +.   Medium-sized, long-tailed, diurnal owl.   <u>When sitting body is more inclined and not so erect as in other owls</u>; occasionally bobs tail.   Upper parts blackish,  spotted with white; under parts whitish, barred with brown and with dark band   over breast; blackish "side-burns" on grayish-white face.   Winter visitor.

TC
Conif.

**101.** SAW-WHET OWL (Aegolius acadicus). 7-8"; robin -. A small owl without ear tufts. Upper parts brown, spotted with white; under parts white, marked with wide brown stripes. Tail short. Notes: a rasping "say-ee"; also bell-like hoot uttered every few seconds. Resident in forests.

TCH
Conif.

**102.** PYGMY OWL (Glaucidium gnoma). 7"; sparrow +. Smallest owl in area. Rusty brown above, with small white spots; white below; narrowly streaked with dark brownish. Relatively long tail marked with whitish cross-bars; no ear tufts. Notes: rapid mellow whistles, ending with 3 detached deliberate notes: "too-too-too-.... took, took, took", seconds apart. Resident in mountain forests.

TCH
Conif.
Sub-Alp.

**103.** BURROWING OWL (Speotyto cunicularia). 9-10"; robin+. Small long-legged round-headed earless owl with brownish-tan upper parts heavily dotted with white and whitish under parts spotted and barred with brownish; white line over eye; short stubby tail. Bobs when disturbed; diurnal. A summer resident in low arid places.

T
Grass
Sage

**104.** GREAT GRAY OWL (Strix nebulosa). 24-33"; crow +. Large earless yellow-eyed owl with heavily striped and mottled grayish plumage. Large facial disks with dark concentric rings around eyes. Irregular.

CH
Conif.
Sub-Alp.

104.

GOATSUCKERS AND SWIFTS

**105.** NIGHTHAWK (Chordeiles minor). 8-10"; robin size. Slender long-winged black-mottled, grayish bird seen hawking with erratic wing-beats for insects high in twilight air; white wing patches near wing-tips.

TCH
Air
Rocks

105.

107.

**106.** POOR-WILL (Phalaenoptilus nuttallii). 7-8"; robin -. Similar, but with rounded wings, white-tipped

T
Brush
Rocks

tail, and no white wing patches. Nocturnal; flies low over ground, hunting night insects; utters soft "poor-will-up" at twilight and dawn. Summer.

TC
Conif.
Air
Rocks

107. VAUX'S SWIFT (Chaetura vauxi). (Picture on p. 83.) 4-5"; sparrow -. Small dark-brown swallow-like bird with long slightly-curved wings. Twinkling bat-like flight is distinctive of swifts. Utters twittering "chip-chip-chip-chip" cry. Summer resident in forested areas.

TC
Rocks
Conif.
Air

108. BLACK SWIFT (Cypseloides niger). 7"; sparrow +. Large black swift with slightly forked tail. Long narrow sickle-shaped wings; flies and glides at great speed. Notes: loud high-pitched twitter. Scattered resident.

T
Rocks
Air

109. WHITE-THROATED SWIFT (Aeronautes saxatilis). 7"; sparrow +. Black-and-white body, with dark upper parts, white sides of rump, belly, throat and face; sooty sides. Swift, twinkling flight. Rocky dry canyons.

## HUMMINGBIRDS

TCH
Brush
Sub-Alp.

110. RUFOUS HUMMINGBIRD (Selasphorus rufus). 3-4"; warbler -. ♂ has upper parts irridescent reddish-brown, throat bright red, breast white, belly brownish. ♀ similar, but more greenish and without solid red throat (whitish, streaked with red, instead). Notes: a light "tschick" and a low "tut-tut-tut-turr", by courting ♂. Common migrant and breeder.

110.

TCH
Brush
Sub-Alp.

111. CALLIOPE HUMMINGBIRD (Stellula calliope). 3"; warbler -. A tiny hummer, smaller than the Rufous. ♂ has white throat, streaked with long reddish lance-shaped feathers; top of head and back greenish; under parts whitish; flanks dusky green. ♀ similar to ♀ Rufous, but smaller and with less reddish-brown on tail. Breeder in mountains.

TC
Brush

112. BLACK-CHINNED HUMMINGBIRD (Archilochus alexandri). 3-4"; warbler -. Characterized by black upper throat and white collar across lower throat extending back to below ears. Belly dusky; back green. ♀ is greenish above and whitish below. Scattered breeder in our region.

TC
Brush

113. BROAD-TAILED HUMMINGBIRD (Selasphorus platycercus). 4"; warbler -. ♂ with greenish upper parts, bright red throat and whitish under parts. ♀ difficult to separate in field from other species. Distinctive trilling sound made by wings in flight. Summer resident.

## KINGFISHER AND WOODPECKERS

TCH
Water
Rocks

114. BELTED KINGFISHER (Megaceryle alcyon). 11-14"; robin +. Large bluish bird with whitish under parts; band of blue (blue and brown in ♀) across the breast; loose crest; long heavy bill; white tail. Notes: a loud, rattling "kleck-kleck-kleck-kleck", etc. Common breeder along streams.

115.          114.

118.     120.

115.  RED-SHAFTED FLICKER (Colaptes cafer).  13-14"; dove size.
Large woodpecker with brown back and wings barred by black; grayish-white
under parts, black collar, grayish head, reddish under surface of wings and
tail, and white rump patch. Mating call: "wick-wick-wick-wick-" & so on;
other calls "wick-up, wick up" (series), and "pee-up" (single).

TCH
Conif.
Sub-Alp.

116.  YELLOW-SHAFTED FLICKER (Colaptes auratus).  12-13"; dove
-.  Similar to Red-shafted Flicker, but with yellowish under surface of wings
and tail and red patch across back of head.  Similar notes.  Resident in east.

TC
Conif.

117.  PILEATED WOODPECKER (Dryocopus pileatus). 17-18"; crow-.
Very large black woodpecker with red crest, white stripes down sides of
neck, and large white patches under wings.  Resident in conifers.

TC
Conif.

118.  WILLIAMSON'S SAPSUCKER (Sphyrapicus thyroideus).  9-10";
robin size.  ♂ has upper parts black, except for white stripes above eye and
through cheek, red throat, and white patches on wings and rump; sides mottled; belly yellow.  ♀ black and white zebra-like stripes on back, barred on
sides, brown head, white rump, and yellow belly.  Nasal "chee-r-r-r". Sum.

TC
Conif.
Str. Wd.

119.  LEWIS' WOODPECKER (Asyndesmus lewis).  11"; robin+.  Dark-
colored woodpecker with black back, grayish nape and breast, and red face
and belly.  Flight is crow-like.  Notes: harsh "churr" and a high-pitched
"chee-up".  Open timber; wanders in fall and winter.

TCH
Conif.
Sub-Alp.

TCH
Conif.
Sub-Alp.

120.  HAIRY WOODPECKER (Dendrocopos villosus).  8-10"; robin size.

Medium-sized woodpecker showing much black and white. Black and white stripes on head; upper parts mostly black with white patch in middle of the back; white spots on wings; tail black with white outer tail feathers; under parts dirty white. Widely distributed resident in forested areas.

TC
Conif.
Str. Wd.

121. DOWNY WOODPECKER (Dendrocopos pubescens). 6-7"; sparrow+. Very similar to Hairy Woodpecker (both have red patch on back of head), but much smaller. Resident mostly in deciduous growth at low elevations.

TCH
Conif.
Sub-Alp.

122. NORTHERN THREE-TOED WOODPECKER (Picoides tridactylus). 9"; robin size. Medium-sized woodpecker with black upper parts spotted with white; top of head golden yellow; white markings down center of back; under parts dirty white, heavily mottled on sides with black. Conifers.

TCH
Conif.
Sub-Alp.

123. ARCTIC THREE-TOED WOODPECKER (Picoides arcticus). 9-10"; robin size. Similar to above, but with wholly black shoulders and back.

TC
Conif.

124. WHITE-HEADED WOODPECKER (Dendrocopos albolarvatus). 9"; robin size. Medium-sized woodpecker, wholly black, except for immaculately white head and white wing-patch. Notes: a sharp harsh "witt" or often a series of "witt's" run together in Kingfisher-like rattle. Conifers.

124.     125.

127.         128.

KINGBIRDS AND FLYCATCHERS

TC
Conif.
Brush

125. EASTERN KINGBIRD (Tyrannus tyrannus). 8-9"; robin -. Head and back sooty gray; tail black with white band at tip; throat and under parts

grayish-white. Call: sharp "kip-per"; song: shrill "kr-r-r-r", ree-bee". A summer resident in open wooded areas.

126. WESTERN KINGBIRD (Tyrannus verticalis). 8-9"; robin -. Head and back pale gray; wings brown; tail black, bordered on sides with white; throat and breast grayish; rest of under parts yellow. Notes: a sharp "whit" or "ker-whit". Summer resident in deciduous growth.

*T*
*Woods*

127. SAY'S PHOEBE (Sayornis sayus). 7-8"; robin -. A large flycatcher with dark-brown head, grayish-brown back, black tail, brownish-gray throat and breast, and reddish-brown belly; bill and feet black. Notes: soft "phee-ur" or "pit-pee-ur". Migrant & summer resident, often on farms.

*T*
*Grass*
*Meadow*
*Farms*

128. WRIGHT'S FLYCATCHER (Empidonax affinis). 5-6"; sparrow -. This and the following 4 species are difficult to tell apart. All are small-sparrow-sized birds, usually seen perching upright on tops of limbs from which they dart forth to seize passing insects. Best identified by notes and habitats. This species has a light greenish back, dark greenish-gray head, buffy-gray throat, greenish breast, and buffy belly; light eye-ring and 2 white wing-bars. Notes: sharp "pew-whit", jerky "sec-pit, tsee-e-e, see-wick". Summer resident in mixed woods.

*TC*
*Conif.*
*Str. Wd.*

129. HAMMOND'S FLYCATCHER (Empidonax hammondii). 5-6"; sparrow -. Similar to above, but has darker throat and breast (clear dark gray, instead of buffy gray); head dark gray, back olive gray and belly pale buffy. Notes: a soft colorless "selip, tsurt, se-leep". Breeds in conifers.

*TC*
*Conif.*

130. TRAILL'S FLYCATCHER (Empidonax traillii). 5-6"; sparrow -. Greenish-brown back, grayish breast, dirty white throat, pale buffy belly, light eye-ring; 2 white wing-bars. Bright snappy "areek-ree-pee-oo. " Sum.

*T*
*Brush*
*Str. Wd.*

131. WESTERN FLYCATCHER (Empidonax difficilis)5-6"; sparrow size. Greenish-brown back, yellowish under parts, white eye-ring. Notes: a rising series of "tsee-tik, tseep, tsee-eet". Summer resident in mixed woods.

*TC*
*Conif.*

132. OLIVE-SIDED FLYCATCHER (Nuttallornis borealis). 7-8", sparrow +. Large dark-colored flycatcher, usually seen perching at or near top of tall dead tree. Narrow white stripe down front from throat to belly separating dark chest patches; Notes: ringing "pip, pee-up, pew". Summer.

*TCH*
*Conif.*
*Sub-Alp.*

133. WESTERN WOOD PEWEE (Contopus sordidulus). 6-7"; sparrow +. Dark grayish-brown above, dirty white throat and belly, grayish breast. Notes: a mild melancholy descending "pee-eer" or hoarse rising "pee-ee" or "pee-ah-wee". Summer resident.

*TCH*
*Conif.*
*Str. Wd.*

HORNED LARK

134. HORNED LARK (Eremophila alpestris). 7-8"; sparrow +. Plump

*TCHA*
*Grass*
*Sage*
*Sub-Alp.*
*Alpine*

132.

brownish bird with black collar below a yellow or white throat; head conspicuously marked with black and yellow or white; grayish-white to yellowish under parts contrasting with black tail; usually seen walking (not hoping) in fields, shores, or other barren areas. Notes: a sharp quick "sliksleesik; and a twittering "tsip, tsip, tsee-dee-dee". Breeds in open areas at all elevations; migrant and winter resident at lower levels.

134.

138.

TCH
Rocks
Air

135. VIOLET-GREEN SWALLOW (Tachycineta thalassina). 5"; sparrow size. Crown, nape and back dark green; wings and tail violet-green; face, breast, belly, and sides of rump white, especially visible in flight. Notes: twittering "tsee-tseet, tseet-tseet", etc. Very common migrant and summer resident, though irregular.

T
Air
Banks

135.

136. BANK SWALLOW (Riparia riparia). 5"; sparrow -. Grayish-brown above; whitish below, a dark band across breast. Nest in banks, etc.

T
Air
Water
Rocks

137. ROUGH-WINGED SWALLOW (Stelgidopteryx ruficollis). 5-6"; sparrow size. Upper parts dark brown; breast and throat light ashy brown; rest of lower parts white. Most likely to be mistaken for Bank Swallow, but lacks clear white under parts and distinct "collar" of that species. The notes: a sharp "pritt". Summer resident, mainly near water.

T
Fields

138. TREE SWALLOW (Tachycineta bicolor). 5-6"; sparrow size. Head (except throat) and back bluish-black; wings and tail greenish-brown; throat, breast and belly white. Similar to Violet-green Swallow, but lacks white rump patches. Notes: a soft "silip" and a series of phrases, as "tsip, prup, tsip, prrup-purp, tsip-pr-r-up", etc. Sum.

TC
Bldgs.
Air
Rocks

139.

139. CLIFF SWALLOW (Petrochelidon pyrrhonota). 5-6"; sparrow size.

Distinguished from other swallows by tan rump-patch, square tail, buffy forehead, reddish face, mottled throat, white belly, and steel black wings and back. Notes: a short low "chur" and a dry twittering sounding like the squeaking of a rusty door. Nests mainly buildings. Summer resident.

140. BARN SWALLOW (Hirundo rustica). 6-7"; sparrow size. Upper parts bluish-black; throat and breast brick red; belly orange. Only swallow in our area with deeply forked tail. Sharp "kvik,kvik-kvik" notes. Summer.

T
Bldgs.
Air
Water

## JAYS, MAGPIES, CROWS

141.      142.

141. CANADA JAY (Perisoreus canadensis). 9-11"; robin +. Robust grayish bird with grayish-white head, black nape, and dark grayish back and tail; under parts light gray; bill short and black. Like a gray ghost in the woods. Notes: soft querulous "whee-oo" or raucous "horee".

CH
Conif.
Sub-Alp.

142. STELLER'S JAY (Cyanocitta stelleri). 12-13"; dove size. Long tail and pointed crest distinctive. Head, neck and shoulders blackish; rest of body dark blue. Shows jay-like curiosity and aggressiveness. Flat gliding flight. Notes: harsh "shack, shack, shack" or "flitch-flitch-flitch."

TCH
Conif.
Sub-Alp.

143. PINYON JAY (Gymnorhinus cyanocephalus). 10-11"; robin +. Color dull grayish-blue, with darker blue crown, and white streaks on throat. Notes: a nasal "kay-uh" and various other sounds. Arid areas in flocks.

TC
Jun-Mah.
Str. Wd.

144. BLACK-BILLED MAGPIE (Pica pica). 18-21" crow -. Large black and white bird with long sweeping tail; blue patches on wings; bill and feet black. Notes: "eck", "bay-bee", "charr", and particularly nasal "maag, maag, maag". Resident.

TCH
Brush
Sage

145. COMMON CROW (Corvus brachyrhynchos). 17-20". Entirely black; flies with wings angled up. A loud insistent "caw" note. Common resident in low country, preferring farming areas.

T
Farms

144.

TCH
Rocks
Conif.

146. RAVEN (Corvus corax). 21-26"; crow +. Large black bird, as big as a hawk. The raven flies hawk-like, alternating flapping with soaring on horizontal wings. Tail wedge-shaped. Notes: loud harsh "krawk" or "kr-r-ruck". Common resident.

146.

147.

H.
Sub-Alp.

147. CLARK'S NUTCRACKER (Nucifraga columbiana). 12-13"; robin +. A jay-like bird slightly larger than Steller's Jay. Body grayish with black wings (white wing-patches) and black tail bordered with white. Notes: a rough grating "kra-a-a". Resident in high alpine areas, lower in winter.

## CHICKADEES, NUTHATCHES AND CREEPER

148.

150.

151.

152.

154.

148. **BLACK-CAPPED CHICKADEE** (Parus atricapillus). 4-5"; war- TC
bler size. Chickadees are tiny birds with very short bills, dark crowns Conif.
and bibs, and white sides of faces. This species has black cap and bib, Str. Wd.
white cheeks, gray back, and dirty white under parts. Notes: clear "chick-
a-dee-dee-dee", and whistled "hee-hee, heer, heer" song. Resident.

149. **CHESTNUT-BACKED CHICKADEE** (Parus rufescens). 4-5"; warbler size. Similar to Black-capped, but has reddish back, dark brownish TC
crown and bib, and brown sides. Notes: a harsh "check-check", more na- Conif.
sal "chickadee" note, but no whistled "spring song." Northwest of region.

150. **MOUNTAIN CHICKADEE** (Parus gambeli). 5"; warbler +. Similar to Black-capped, but has white line through cap over each eye. Back, CH
sides, and wings grayish-brown. Notes: "chickadee" similar to the other Conif.
chickadees, but slower and more nasal, as "zickadya, dya, dya"; the spring Sub-Alp.
song, a loud whistled "hee-heeee, hoo-hoooo". Resident in conifers.

151. **RED-BREASTED NUTHATCH** (Sitta canadensis). 4-5"; warbler
size. Nuthatches are chunky little birds, smaller than sparrows, often seen
creeping up or (usually) down the bark of trees or ranging along a branch TC
hunting for insects. Tail very short. This species is a small nuthatch with Conif.
black head and white line over eye; rest of upper parts bluish-gray; under
parts reddish-brown. Nasal "nyenk, nyenk, nyenk" cry. Resident.

152. **WHITE-BREASTED NUTHATCH** (Sitta carolinensis). 5-6"; sparrow size. Large nuthatch with black crown and nape, bluish-gray back, and TCH
white sides of head, shoulders, and under parts. Notes: nasal "tan, tan", a Conif.
low mellow "too-too-too-too", and a sharp nasal "keer, keer". Resident. Sub-Alp.

153. **PYGMY NUTHATCH** (Sitta pygmaea). 4"; warbler -. Small nuthatch with brownish-gray head, bluish-gray back, black ear-patch, white TC
spot on nape, and buffy under parts. Notes: a moderate "kit, kit, kit", in Conif.
flocking; a rapid "ti-di, ti-di, ti-di". Resident; fond of yellow pine forest.

154. **BROWN CREEPER** (Certhia familiaris). 5-6"; warbler size. A
small black-streaked brownish warbler-sized bird with with long curved bill TCH
and a long tail; whitish below. Usually seen creeping up bark of a tree trunk, Conif.
looking like bark. Call: faint sustained "tsee" or "tsick"; song: weak lisp- Sub-Alp.
ing series of "tsee-tsee-tsee-ti-ti-tsee" on several pitches. Resident.

## DIPPER AND WRENS

155. **DIPPER** (Cinclus mexicanus).
7-8"; robin -. Dark slate-colored bird,
looking like large chunky wren. Conspicuous white eyelid and short stubby TCH
tail. Seen in or near water, often bob- Water
bing or dipping body. Call: loud insistent "jigic, jigic, jigic". Loud clear
wren-like song. Resident by water. 155.

157.            156.

**156. WINTER WREN** (<u>Troglodytes</u> <u>troglodytes</u>). 4"; warbler -. Wrens are small nervous brownish birds with slender bills and with tails rakishly carried almost straight up over back. Solitary in habits, but aggressive in personality. This species is a <u>small dark solid-brown wren with short stubby tail</u>. Often sneaks through brush and over logs like a brown mouse. Resident.

TC
Conif.

**157. ROCK WREN** (<u>Salpinctes</u> <u>obsoletus</u>). 5-6"; warbler size. Grayish-colored wren with <u>grayish-brown white-spotted back,</u> <u>white stripe over eye</u>, buffy-white corners at end of tail, grayish breast finely streaked with brownish, and pale grayish belly. Call: loud "tick-eer"; song: "tee-oo, tee-oo, tee-oo", or sounding like "cheep-oo, cheep-oo, cheep-oo, -". Resident.

TCH
Rocks

**158. HOUSE WREN** (<u>Troglodytes</u> <u>aedon</u>). 4-5"; warbler size. Medium-sized wren, <u>brownish above with black and white spots on rump; wings and tail barred with blackish and faint line over eye</u>. Under parts pale brown on throat and breast and dirty-white belly; no white in tail and facial markings very faint. Call: harsh rasping notes, as a scolding "chur" or "chee". Song: rapid "tsee-tsee, wheedle, wheedle, wheedle, widdle-widdle-". Sum.

T
Brush
Bldg.

**159. LONG-BILLED MARSH WREN** (<u>Cistothorus</u> <u>palustris</u>). 4-5"; warbler size. <u>White line over eye and conspicuous black and white striping on back</u>. Call: harsh "churr, churr, churr"; song: preliminary loud "tuk-tuk-tuk" followed by explosion of clicking, buzzing, sputtering sounds. Summer.

T
Marsh

## MIMIC THRUSHES

161. 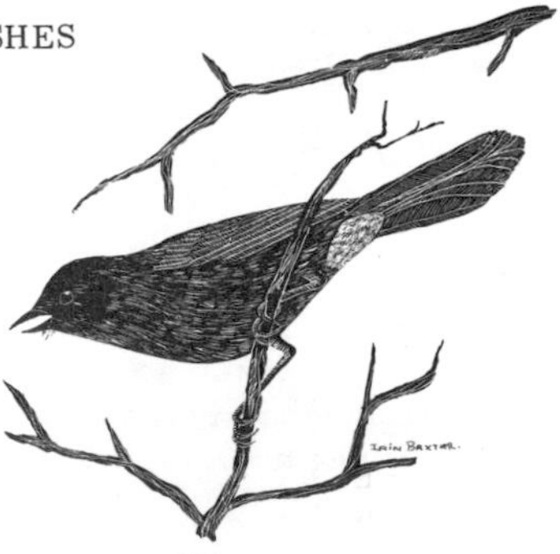                  160.

160. CATBIRD (Dumetella carolinensis). 8-9"; robin -. Blackish-gray bird with black cap and reddish-brown patch at base of tail underneath. Call: a mellow "phut, phut" and a cat-like "may-ee". Song: variable and often mimicking other songsters. Common bird in gardens. Summer.

T
Brush
Woods

161. SAGE THRASHER (Oreoscoptes montanus). 8-9"; robin -. Upper parts grayish-brown with white line over eye and narrow dark streaks on buffy face; throat white; under parts buffy-white, heavily streaked, particularly on breast, with small brownish spots. Bill straight and slender. It frequently jerks tail when perching. Call: low "chuck, chuck" and whistled "whee-er". Song: loud clear rapid series or repeated warbles. Resident.

T
Sage

THRUSHES

162.                                   163.

162. ROBIN (Turdus migratorius). 8-10". Head, wings and tail dark gray. White streaks on throat; back dark grayish; bill yellow; underparts brick red. Usually flips tail on alighting. Calls: various short sharp notes. Song: familiar series of rising and falling phrases; usually 4 in number and repeated many times. Summer resident in lowlands; a few in winter.

TCH
Meadows
Urban
Conif.
Sub-Alp.

163. HERMIT THRUSH (Hylocichla guttata). 7"; sparrow +. The following thrushes are shy woodland or forest birds with pleasing flute-like songs and actions similar to Robin's. This species is a shy brown-backed bird with slender bill, spotted breast (large sooty-brown spots arranged in streaks), and reddish tail and rump; throat and breast white or buffy. Call: a whistled "chee" or low "chuck"; song: a series of detached trilled phrases, each introduced by prolonged clear flute-like note of high quality. Summer.

H
Sub-Alp.

164. RUSSET-BACKED THRUSH (Hylocichla ustulata). 7"; sparrow +. Shy brownish-green-backed bird with slender bill, and spotted breast. Like Hermit Thrush, but tail brownish-green, not red; throat and breast buffy. Calls: a querulous "quirt" and whinnying "ker-whee-ee-ee". Song: melodious series of flute-like notes, as "wher-where, wheelia, wheelia"; the 2 introductory notes on same pitch, but each of following phrases spirals upward. Summer resident in brushy areas of lowland and mt. forests.

TCH
Brush
Str. Wd.
Conif.

165. VEERY (Hylocichla fuscescens). 7"; sparrow +. Shy thrush with cinnamon-brown upper parts and grayish under parts faintly spotted on the breast. Notes: a coarse "vee-ew". Song: loud whistled descending "vee-er, vee-er, vee-er". Summer resident in woods along streams.

TC
Str. Wd.

166.

167.

169

170.

173.

172.

166. VARIED THRUSH (Ixoreus naevius). 9-10"; robin size. Similar to Robin, but has orange eye-stripe and wing-bars and black band across salmon-red breast; rest of head, back and tail bluish slate. Low "cherk" call; song: a slow series of detached drawn-out notes, each on a different pitch, resembling single notes blown on harmonica. Resident in northwest.

TC
Conif.

167. MOUNTAIN BLUEBIRD (Sialia currucoides). 6-7"; sparrow+. ♂ has upper parts sky blue; throat and breast grayish blue; belly grayish buff. ♀ has blue of ♂ replaced by greenish-gray; rump bluish-gray. Calls: soft low "pew" or "chur". Song: short clear caroling warble. Summer resident.

TH
Grass
Sub-Alp.
Alpine

168.  WESTERN BLUEBIRD (Sialia mexicana).  6-7"; sparrow+.  ♂ with
upper parts, including head and throat, blue; breast, sides and upper back
reddish.  ♀ similar, but paler; blue on head and back replaced by grayish.
Notes: mild, whistled "pew, pew, pew".  Irregular summer resident.

T
Fields

169.  TOWNSEND'S SOLITAIRE (Myadestes townsendi).  8-9", robin -.
Dark greenish gray in color with white eye-ring; tail black with white outer feathers; buffy patch in middle of black wings.  Resembles flycatcher in
habits (see p. 87).  Call: single metallic "keek".  Song: a sustained irregular  finch-like warble.  Summer resident; a few winter in lowlands.

TCH
Conif.
Sub-Alp.
Jun. Mah.

KINGLETS (constant rapid flitting of wings)

170.  GOLDEN-CROWNED KINGLET (Regulus satrapa).  3-4"; warbler
-.  Upper parts greenish-gray; under parts brownish-white; white line over
eye, crown red (yellow in ♀), bordered by yellow.  Call:  thin high   "see,
see, see".  Song: rising series of thin "sees", dropping into a chatter at
the end.  Resident in coniferous forests, descending in winter.

TC
Conif.
Str. Wd.

171.  RUBY-CROWNED KINGLET (Regulus calendula).  3-4';  warbler
-.  Upper parts grayish-gren; under parts buffy white; eye-ring and wing-
bars white; center of crown red in ♂ (but not often seen).   Call:  a sharp
"chit-it".  Song: a rapid "tee-tee-tee-tew-tew, wher-her-hee, wher-her-
hee".  Summer resident in woods and forests.

TC
Conif.
Str. Wd.

PIPIT (walks instead of hops).

172.  WATER PIPIT (Anthus spinoletta).  6-7"; sparrow size.  Bill slender (unlike thick bill of similar-looking sparrow).   Upper parts grayish-
brown; tail dark with white outer feathers, light line over eye; under parts
buffy, streaked on breast and sides with dusky.  When on ground, constant-
ly bobs tail.  Call: short sharp "tsee-seep".   Song: a stacatto series of
"chee-weets".  Summer resident above timber; migrant, winter visitor lower.

THA
Open
Fields
Alpine

WAXWINGS AND SHRIKES

173.  CEDAR WAXWING (Bombycilla cedrorum).  6-7"; sparrow+.   A
sleek brown bird with long pointed crest, black mask and chin, plain dark
brown wings, and broad yellow band at tip of tail.  A high thin lisped "zee"
note.  Summer resident in lowlands.

T
Brush

174.  BOHEMIAN WAXWING (Bombycilla garrula).  7-8"; robin -.  Similar to above, but larger, grayer,  with
white and yellow markings on wings.  A
low trilled whistled note.  Winter visitor.

T
Woods

175.  LOGGERHEAD SHRIKE (Lan-
ius ludovicianus).  9" robin -.  Shrikes
are grayish robin-sized birds  with
black masks through eyes, black wings,    175.

T
Sage
Fields
Brush

and black tails  with white outer tail-feathers.  Usually seen quietly perching on upper branches or spires of trees, light wires, or posts.  The Logerhead Shrike has a clear gray breast; various musical phrases.  Summer.

T
Open
Areas     **176.  NORTHERN SHRIKE (Lanius excubitor).**  9-10"; robin size.  Larger than Loggerhead Shrike and with fine wavy lines on breast.  Winter vis.

## VIREOS AND WARBLERS

177.

180.

182.

181.

183.

185.

185A.

187.

177. WARBLING VIREO (Vireo gilvus). 5-6"; warbler +. Vireos are small greenish-or grayish-backed warbler-like birds, hunting for insects like warblers among leaves and twigs, but slower and less active. Bill is heavier than that of warblers, but best identified by vocal notes. This species has gray crown, grayish-green upper parts, and whitish under parts; indistinct white line, unbordered by black, over eye. Call: a buzzy "twee". Song: squeaky wavery "zeekery, zeekery, zeekery, zeek". Summer res.

T
Woods
Str. Wd.

178. SOLITARY VIREO (Vireo solitarius). 5-6"; warbler +. Greenish-backed vireo with dark gray head, white eye-ring, 2 white wing-bars, and dirty white under parts. Call: a low purring note. Song: series of detached queries and answers as "wee-ee, tsiweeoo, reet-tee, ptic, peeteewee, pisoor", and so forth. Summer resident.

T
Woods
Conif.

179. RED-EYED VIREO (Vireo olivaceus). 5-6"; warbler +. Greenish backed vireo with black bordered white line over eye, dark gray crown, and white under parts; no wing-bars. Call: a querulous "quee". Song: monotonous series of questions and answers like Solitary Vireo's, but lower in pitch, more regular, and in faster tempo. Sings in tree tops. Summer res.

T
Str. Wd.

180. YELLOW WARBLER (Dendroica petechia). 4-5". Warblers are slender brightly-colored very active birds that are smaller than sparrows ( except Chat) and usually show considerable yellow in plumage. This species is the only all-yellow appearing warbler in our region. Light greenish wash on back (darker in ♀). Call: a sharp "chip". Song: rapid clear variable "chwee, chwee, chwee, zee-zee-zee. " Summer resident.

T
Woods
Str. Wd.

181. ORANGE-CROWNED WARBLER (Vermivora celata). 4-5". Light green upper parts and yellow-green underparts; faint orange crown. Call: sharp "chip". Song: weak trill, dropping in pitch and volume at end. Summer.

T
Brush

182. AUDUBON'S WARBLER (Dendroica auduboni). 4-5". Grayish and blackish, with yellow crown, rump, throat, and side-patches. Call: moderate "tchip". Song: like that of Yellow, but richer and rising in pitch. Sum.

TC
Conif.

183. TOWNSEND'S WARBLER (Dendroica townsendi). 4-5". Crown, throat and broad line through eye black; rest of face yellow; back greenish; wing and tail black and white; under parts yellow; sides streaked with black. ♀ similar, but with yellow throat. Call: sharp "tsip"; song: clear bright buzzy chant of "zeer-zeer-zeer, zeet-see", first buzzy, then sibilant. Sum.

CH
Conif.
Sub-Alp.

184. NORTHERN WATERTHRUSH (Seiurus noveboracensis). 5-6". A sparrow-sized warbler, brownish above, heavily streaked below, with white line over eye. Call: sharp metallic "tchip". Song: loud rapid descending series, "chewit, chewit, chewit, chew-chew-chew-chewit". Summer in n.

T
Conif.
Marsh

185. YELLOW-BREASTED CHAT (Icteria virens). 6-7"; sparrow size. Large-sparrow-sized warbler with greenish-brown upper parts, a yellow throat and breast, white belly and eye-ring. Call: mellow "kook" or sharp "kee-yuck". Song: various calls and notes, alternating with loud and clear rolling whistle. Summer resident in deciduous growth along streams.

T
Str. Wd.
Brush

(NOTE: warblers on this page are illustrated on page 96.)

**TCH**
**Brush**

185A. MACGILLIVRAY'S WARBLER (Oporornis tolmiei). 4-5" ♂ is a green-backed yellow-bellied warbler with dark gray hood and broken eye-ring. ♀ similar, but paler, especially on throat. Call: a moderate "chuck". Song: a loud "sweeter-sweeter-sweeter-sweet-sweet". Summer.

**TC**
**Conif.**

186. NASHVILLE WARBLER (Vermivora ruficapillis). 4-5". Similar to MacGillivray's, but head lighter gray and with yellow throat. Call: a sharp "tsip". Song: "see-bit, see-bit, see-bit, see-bit, titititi". Summer.

**TC**
**Conif.**

187. WILSON'S WARBLER (Wilsonia pusilla). 4-5". ♂ greenish above, yellow below, with jet-black cap on head. ♀ similar, but with smaller black cap. Call: sharp "tchep". Song: "tcheps" repeated rapidly. Sum. & Mig.

**T**
**Marsh**

188. YELLOWTHROAT (Geothlypis trichas). 4-5". Swamp-inhabiting warbler with black mask through eyes, greenish upper parts, yellow throat and breast, and buffy belly. ♀ lacks black mask. Call: husky "tchek". Song: hurried "rees-wittee, rees-wittee, rees-wittee". Summer; often in cattails.

**T**
**Woods**

189. AMERICAN REDSTART (Setophaga ruticilla). 5". Medium-sized warbler with black head, throat and upper parts, and salmon-red patches on sides, wings, and tail. Upper belly with black and red blotches; lower belly white. ♀ with similar pattern, but colors much paler. Call: sharp "chip". Song: loud bright "tsee, tsee, tsee, tsoo-weet". Migrant and summer res.

### MEADOWLARK, BLACKBIRDS AND ORIOLES

190.    191.    195.    192.

190. WESTERN MEADOWLARK (Sturnella neglecta). 8-10"; robin size. Chunky short-tailed bird with light brown upper parts streaked with black; yellow under parts crossed on breast with black V-shaped collar. Call: a soft "turk". Song: short flute-like gurgling series of phrases, like "eu-hew, wheelicky, wheelicky", rapidly uttered and ventriloqui .l. Common res.

T
Grass
Sage
Fields

191. RED-WINGED BLACKBIRD (Agelaius pheoniceus). 7-9"; robin -. ♂ jet black with red shoulder patches. ♀ brownish heavily striped bird with characteristic blackbird bill and habit of flying from stalk to stalk in marsh. Calls: harsh "keck" or "tee-er". Song: liquid gurgling "o-ker-leer-lup" or "o-ka-lee". Common summer resident at low elevations; few winter.

T
Marsh
Str. Wd.

192. BREWER'S BLACKBIRD (Euphagus cyanocephalus). 8-9"; robin -. ♂ is wholly black blackbird with a white eye. ♀ is entirely brownish-gray with a dark eye. Call: harsh "check" or "chup!" Song: wheezy "kor-ree". Common summer resident; migrates widely; few in winter.

TCH
Open

193. YELLOW-HEADED BLACKBIRD (Xanthocephalus xanthocephalus). 9-10"; robin size. ♂ with head, throat and breast yellow; rest of body black, except for white patch on wing. ♀ mostly dark brown with light line over eye and light yellow throat and upper breast. Call: liquid "klook" or "klack". Song: leering gurgled "c-caow-ow" with variations. Summer resident.

T
Marsh

194. BROWN-HEADED COWBIRD (Molothrus ater). 7-8"; robin -. Like small blackbird with chocolate-brown head (♂) and short sparrow-like bill. ♀ uniformly gray with streaks or stripes. Tail lifted high off ground when walking. Call: short "tchuck"; song: rasping "klug, klug-gleee" or "klug-tseee". Remarkable courtship tricks on light wires. Summer resident.

T
Brush

195. BULLOCK'S ORIOLE (Icterus bullockii). 7-9"; robin -. ♂ is bright orange and black with large white wing-patches and a black bib. ♀ has upper parts grayish, suffused with yellow on head; wings dark with 2 white wing-bars; sides of throat and breast yellow; rest of under parts whitish. Calls: sharp "kip" or "tyew", also sharp chittering "che-che-che-che, " & so forth. Song: accented "kit-kit-tik, kit-tik, whee-oo-wheet". Summer.

T
Woods

196.

IAIN BAATEN.

## TANAGER

196. WESTERN TANAGER (Piranga ludoviciana). 6-7"; sparrow +. ♂ with red head; wings, middle of back, and tail black; rest of body and wing-bars yellow. ♀ with the upper parts greenish-yellow; wings dusky with yellow-white wing-bars; under parts dull yellow. Call: dry "pit-tic". Song: like that of Robin (p. 93), but hoarser and much faster in tempo. Summer resident in coniferous timber. Deliberate actions.

TCH
Conif.

197.

198.

200.

203.

205

207.

197.  EVENING GROSBEAK (Hesperiphona vespertina).  7-8"; sparrow +.  ♂ with head, shoulders, wings and tail dark brown, except for yellow forehead and line over eye and large white patch in wing; rest of body greenish-yellow.  ♀ brownish-gray with black tail and yellow suffusion on under parts; wing black with white patch.  Very large yellow bill distinctive both sexes.  Calls: loud high-pitched "ee-eep", "tsee", or "gr-ree".  Song: irregular short warble.  Summer in mt. forests; migrant & winter elsewhere.

TC
Conif.

198.  PINE GROSBEAK (Pinicola enucleator).  8-9"; robin size.  Large finch of high mountain with stout conical bill and deeply-forked tail.  ♂ with head, breast and rump rosy red; wings (with 2 white wing-bars) and tail

TCH
Conif.
Sub-Alp.

blackish; rest of body gray. ♀ grayish, tinged on head and rump with yellowish or light red; wings (2 white wing-bars) and tail dusky. Calls: clear
whistled "tee-tee-tew", sharp "peer", and low trilled whistle. Song: rich
and melodious warble. Summer resident in high mts.; lower in winter.

199. BLACK-HEADED GROSBEAK (Pheucticus melanocephalus). 7-8";
sparrow +. ♂ with head black; nape and rump reddish; rest of upper parts
and tail black; streaked with whitish; under parts rusty, becoming yellow on
belly. ♀ brownish. Call: sharp "eek". Song: similar to carol of a Robin,
but faster in tempo and more varied. Summer resident in lowlands.

f
Woods

200. LAZULI BUNTING (Passerina amoena). 5"; sparrow -. ♂ with
head, neck, and back bright blue; wings and tail dusky blue; breast reddish;
belly white; wings crossed with 2 white wing-bars. ♀ brownish above, lighter below; wing-bars whitish. Call: sharp "tsip". Song: high-pitched ram-
bling warble made up of several phrases, each on different pitch level. Sum.

T
Brush

201. LARK BUNTING (Calamospiza melanocorys). 6-7"; sparrow +.
♂ black with large white wing-patches. ♀ brown, with striped breast. Call:
sweet "hoo-ee" uttered in flight; song: trilling warble. Breeds mainly in e.

T
Grass

202. SNOW BUNTING (Plectrophenax nivalis). 6-7"; sparrow +. Mostly
white with crown, nape, sides of breast, and back brownish; wings and tail
black and white. Notes: clear whistled "tee-oo", musical rolling whistle.
Winter visitor to low open areas.

T
Fields

203. CASSIN'S FINCH (Carpodacus cassinii). 6"; sparrow size. Reddish sparrow-like bird with bright red crown, pinkish upper parts (streaked
on back with dusky) and whitish under parts, except pinkish throat and breast;
sides and belly not striped. ♀ heavily striped and brownish in color. Call:
finch-like "too-dee-yip". Song: bright chattering warble. Resident.

TC
Conif.

204. HOUSE FINCH (Carpodacus mexicanus). 5-6"; sparrow size. Similar to Cassin's Finch, but smaller; crown, throat and breast red or orange
rather than pinkish. Sides and belly conspicuously striped. Call: coarse
"wheet". Song: long irregular finch-like warble, ending in coarse note.

T
Conif.
Urban

205. GRAY-CROWNED ROSY FINCH (Leucosticte tephrocotis). 6";
sparrow size. ♂ dark brownish sparrow-like bird. Forehead black, chin
dark brown, nape gray, wings and tail black. ♀ similar, but duller, with
gray of head reduced. Calls: loud "pit-pit", harsh "chuck" or "tzzt", twittering flight note. Song: high finch-like warble. Summer resident in high
mountains of northern part of region, descending to lower areas in winter.

HA
Alpine
Rocks

206. BLACK ROSY FINCH (Leucosticte atrata). 6"; sparrow size. It
is similar to above species, but body blackish, instead of brownish. This
species breeds in high mountains, wandering elsewhere in open in winter.

HA
Alpine
Rocks

207. PINE SISKIN (Spinus pinus). 4-5"; warbler size. Small brownish
finch-like bird heavily streaked with dusky; yellow showing in wings and
tail in flight. Notes: high-pitched "pi-ti-tic" in flight, loud "clee-ip", and
drawn-out buzzy "sher-ree-ee". Resident and wanderer in forests.

TCH
Conif.
Sub-Alp.

210.                              211.

213.                              215.

218.              220.

208. COMMON REDPOLL (<u>Acanthis flammea</u>).     5-6"; sparrow size.
<u>Streaked, grayish-brown bird with dark red patch on forehead, black chin,</u>
<u>and white belly.</u>   Rump white with dark streaks.   Call: twittering "chet-
chet".   Song: series of "chets" followed by trill.   Winter visitor.

TCH
Fields

209. HOARY REDPOLL (<u>Acanthis hornemanni</u>).  5"; sparrow -.  Similar to Common Redpoll, but smaller and paler.  Rump white without streaks.
Irregular winter visitor to northern part of our region.

TCH
Fields

210. AMERICAN GOLDFINCH (<u>Spinus tristis</u>).   5"; sparrow -.  ♂, in
<u>spring and summer, bright yellow with black forehead, wings (white wing-</u>
<u>bars), and tail.</u>   In winter, like ♀, but with black and white wings.   ♀ with

T
Fields
Urban
Woods

upper parts brownish-green; wings and tail dark with grayish wing-bars; under parts dull yellow. Calls: rollicking "ker-chik-chik, ker-chiki-chik" given in flight. Song: sustained twittering canary-like warble. Resident.

211. RED CROSSBILL (Loxia curvirostra). 5-6"; sparrow size. ♂ is red with dusky wings and tail. ♀ is dull greenish-gray, lighter on head and rump. Crossed tips of mandibles is characteristic, but seldom seen in field. Call: sharp "kip-kip", kip-kip-kip", often alternated with "chit-chit, zicker-zicker-zeen". Song: finch-like warble. Resident in conifers. — TCH Conif. Sub-Alp.

212. WHITE-WINGED CROSSBILL (Loxia leucoptera). 6-7"; sparrow +. ♂ is rosy red with black wings crossed by 2 broad white wing-bars; tail black. ♀ grayish-green, streaked with black; 2 broad white wing-bars. In field, crossed tips of mandibles seldom visible. Wing-bars separate this species from Red Crossbill when in flight. Calls: soft "peet" or "peet-peet" and dry "chip-chip". Song: irregular series of warblings, interrupted by occasional loud "seet". Irregular winter visitor. — TCH Conif. Sub-Alp.

## TOWHEES AND JUNCOS

213. RUFOUS-SIDED TOWHEE (Pipilo erythrophthalmus). 7-8"; robin -. Somewhat like Robin in color pattern and forages mainly on ground. ♂ with head and upper parts black, with numerous white spots on wings; sides reddish; belly white. ♀ similar, but head dark brown. Conspicuous red eye. Call: complaining nasal "me-ay-ee" or "ma-reeee". Song: rather colorless "chiddle-chiddle-chiddle-chiddle"; notes variable, rather buzzy. Sum. — T Brush

214. GREEN-TAILED TOWHEE (Chlorura chlorura). 6-7"; sparrow+. Small towhee with red crown and otherwise green upper parts; breast gray, throat and belly white. Call: sharp "chink"; song: distinctive and accented "weet-chur, chee, churr". Summer resident in brush. — TC Brush

215. OREGON JUNCO (Junco oreganus). 5-6"; sparrow size. Juncos are sparrow-like birds with conspicuous white outer tail feathers, black or grayish heads, and white bills. This species has black head, reddish sides and rusty-red back. ♀ has gray sides. Call: sharp "chek"; song: a simple trill, similar to that of Chipping Sparrow (p. 105), but more musical. Res. — TCH Brush Sub-Alp. Conif.

216. PINK-SIDED JUNCO (Junco mearnsi). 5-6"; sparrow size. Similar to Oregon, but has gray head, dull brown back and pink sides. Call and song: similar to Oregon Junco's. Summer; winter visitor in southern areas. — CH Conif.

217. SLATE-COLORED JUNCO (Junco hyemalis). 6"; sparrow size. A junco with uniform blackish-gray head, breast, sides, wings and back; belly white. Notes: very similar to Oregon Junco's. Uncommon in winter. — T Open Brush

## SPARROWS

218. SAVANNAH SPARROW (Passerculus sandwichensis). 5-6". Sparrows are small compact birds with short conical canary-like bills. This species is a small, light-colored, heavily-streaked sparrow with a yellow — TH Grass Fields Sub-Alp.

line over the eye, a white line through the center of the crown, and notched tail. Call: a soft "tssit". Song: faint insect-like "tset-tset-tsa-wzzzzzt-subut" or tzeet-tzeet-tsa-tzeee-tsay". Summer resident; a few in winter.

**219. GRASSHOPPER SPARROW** (Ammodramus savannarum).    4-5".
T
Grass
Small sparrow with short tail, similar to Savannah Sparrow, but no streaks on breast. Back strongly striped. Song: insect-like "tseet-tsee-tzeee."

**220  VESPER SPARROW** (Pooecetes gramineus). (Picture on p. 102).
T
Meadow
Fields
5-6". A bird of meadows and open farm lands, resembling pale Song Sparrow or Savannah Sparrow, but showing conspicuous white outer tail feathers in flight. Song: similar to Song Sparrow's, but opening notes not hurried (first 2 soft and low; second 2 higher in pitch). Summer resident.

222.            224.

228.    225.

229.              230.

221. SAGE SPARROW (Amphispiza belli). 5-6". Grayish sparrow with dark spot in middle of breast and white streak on each side of throat. Song: soft "tsit-tsoo-tseee-tsay". Summer resident in southern part of region.  
T Sage

222. CHIPPING SPARROW (Spizella passerina). 5". Small sparrow with clear gray under parts, bright red cap, white line over eye, and black line through eye; back brown, streaked with black. Call: faint "tsip"; song: dry rapidly-uttered monotonous series of "chips", on one pitch. Summer.  
T Woods

223. TREE SPARROW (Spizella arborea). 6". Similar to Chipping, but may be separated from it by larger size, single round black spot in center of breast, 2 distinct white wing-bars, black and yellow bill, & winter season.  
T Open

224. BREWER'S SPARROW (Spizella breweri). 5". Small pale sparrow with finely streaked crown and unstreaked pale-gray breast. Song: canary-like series of trills on varying pitches. Summer resident.  
T Sage Brush Grass

225. WHITE-CROWNED SPARROW (Zonotrichia leucophrys). 5-6". Crown conspicuously striped with black and white; clear gray throat and under parts, grayish-brown back streaked with dark. Call: sharp "tsip"; song: slow, plaintive, nasal series of notes as "say-chi-di-seeee-say". Summer.  
TCH Woods Conif. Sub-Alp.

226. HARRIS'S SPARROW (Zonotrichia querula). 7-8". Large sparrow with black chin and throat, dusky-grayish crown, whitish face (back of eye), brownish back (streaked on shoulders with dark), and whitish under parts heavily streaked. 2 white wing-bars. Call: metallic "spink!" Migr. & winter.  
T Woods

227. WHITE-THROATED SPARROW (Zonotrichia albicollis). 6-7". Resembles White-crowned, but has conspicuous white throat and a yellow spot between eye and bill. Call: harsh "chink" and slurred "tseet". Song: plaintive series of whistles, much like "Oh, Sam, Peabody-Peabody." Migr. in e.  
T Woods

228. LINCOLN SPARROW (Melospiza lincolnii). 5-6". Like pale Song Sparrow, but grayish throat bordered by black lines, buffy band (with narrow black streaks) across breast, small dark spot in middle of breast, and grayish-brown upper parts dark-streaked. Very shy. Call: sharp "chek". Sweet gurgling rolling song, rising in pitch and then dropping. Sum. &migr.  
CH Sub-Alp. Meadow

229. SONG SPARROW (Melospiza melodia). 6". Dark streaked on grayish-brown above; dark brown streaked on white below; dark spot in middle of breast. Call: sharp "chwick" or a soft "seet!". starts with "chit-chit-chit-chawee" followed by various runs & trills. Resident.  
TCH Brush Woods Str. Wd.

230. FOX SPARROW (Passerella iliaca). 6-7". Large plump sparrow with clear gray-brown above; white below is streaked with dark brown spots, which meet in large dark blotch in mid-breast; reddish tail. Calls: "tseet" or soft "tsook"; sharp "tchek". Song: loud and brilliant. Summer, migr. & winter.  
CH Brush Str. Wd. Sub-Alp.

231. Lapland Longspur

## COMMON REPTILES

Unlike amphibians, which have moist smooth and slimy skins, the bodies of reptiles are dry and covered with scales. By this feature alone any reptile in our area may be known. Three general kinds are encountered in our region: turtles, lizards and snakes. With the exception of turtles, reptiles usually occur in dry habitats. All reptiles may bite when handled, but of the species you will meet in our region, only the rattlesnake is poisonous. Like amphibians, reptiles hibernate in cold weather, come out in warm. .

T
Marsh
Water

1. PAINTED TURTLE (Chrysemys picta). 5-9". Practically the only turtle in our area, this species has a dark greenish or brownish carapace (upper shell) marked with a broken network of yellow lines. Plastron (lower shell) with large dark central patch bordered by orange; legs and tail dark, marked with yellow. Head also dark, but striped with yellow and red. In water.

1.

T
Sage
Rocks
Jun-Mah.

2. SAGEBRUSH LIZARD (Sceloporus graciosus). Body 2-2 1/2"long. A small lizard with light brown upper parts marked by a longitudinal row of dark brown spots along each side of back; sides orange or yellow; under parts gray with blue patches on sides of belly. Southern part of region.

T
Sage
Rocks

3. SHORT-HORNED LIZARD (Phrynosoma douglassi). Body 2 1/2-3 1/2" long. Commonly called "horned toad". Color variable, from grayish to brownish or yellowish, marked above with rows of dark spots. A fringe of spines along side of body and on tail; horny spines at back of head short and blunt. In sandy or rocky areas.

3.       2.

===============================================================

## CONCLUSION OF BIRD SECTION

231. LAPLAND LONGSPUR (Calcarius lapponicus). 6-7";. sparrow +.
Sparrow-like bird with brownish upper parts streaked with black, brownish nape, and whitish or buffy under parts streaked with small black spots along sides, forming collar across throat. Tail black, edged with white. Notes: rattling, twittering series of "chirs"; whistled "too-ee". Winter.

T
Fields

4. WESTERN SKINK (Eumeces skiltonianus). Body 2 1/2-3 1/4" long. Slender body, long tapering tail, and small legs. Brownish above with longitudinal light and dark stripes along sides of back; pattern paler on tail. A young skink similar, but with bright blue tail (blue tail occasionally found in adults). Usually under rocks or logs.

TC
Rocks
Woods
Brush

4.

5. NORTHERN ALLIGATOR LIZARD (Gerrhonotus coeruleus). Body 3 1/2-5" long. Smooth-appearing body with fold of skin along each side distinctive. Dark greenish above with checkered patterns of small dark and light spots; under parts whitish with dark longitudinal stripes along edges of scale rows. In logs or rocks or leaf mold in woods of north of region.

TC
Rocks
Woods

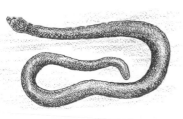

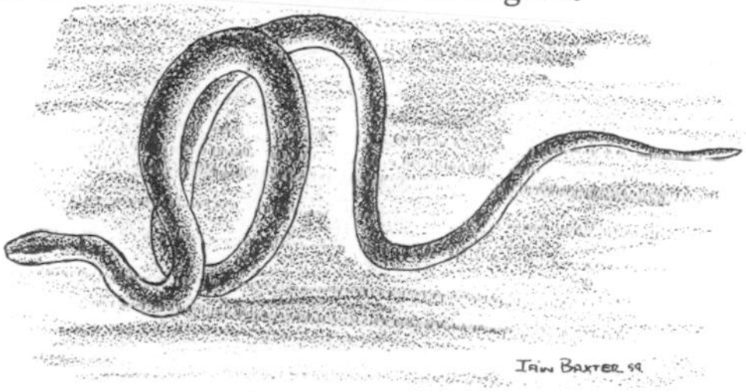

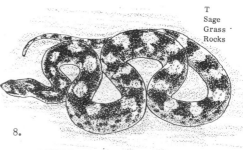

6.                              7.

6. RUBBER BOA (Charina bottae). Length, 12-25". Small harmless and slow-moving snake with small head and blunt tip of tail. Upper parts clear unmarked greenish or brownish; under parts whitish or yellowish. Rubbery appearance. Feeds on mice and lizards which it kills by constriction. Active mostly at night, though occasionally by day, in moist woods.

TCH
Rocks
Conif.
Woods

7. RACER (Coluber constrictor). Length 30-50". Long slender snake with gradually tapering tail. Colors variable; upper parts clear unmarked bluish, grayish or brownish; under parts unmarked grayish, bluish, whitish or yellowish, but usually lighter than upper parts. Noted for speed of movement, these snakes feed on frogs, lizards, snakes, birds, birds' eggs and insects. Open grassy or brushy places at low to moderate elevations.

T
Grass
Rocks
Sage

8. GOPHER SNAKE (Pituophis catenifer). Length, 36-72". Large aggressive non-poisonous snake. Upper parts pale brownish or buffy (or whitish) with longitudinal series of dark brown or black blotches on body and tail; white to yellowish below with scattered small blotches. Common in arid places, feeding on small mammals, birds and lizards.

T
Sage
Grass
Rocks

8.

**9. COMMON GARTER SNAKE** (Thamnophis sirtalis). Length, 24-30".
Slender medium-sized snake, dark grayish or brownish above with 3 longituidinal light stripes running along the back and sides. Conspicuous red blotches along sides. Under parts yellowish or grayish anteriorly, becoming darker posteriorly. Pugnacious but harmless, though often releasing foul-smelling contents of anal glands. Usually near water.

TC
Str. Wd.
Marsh

9.                          10.

**10. WESTERN GARTER SNAKE** (Thamnophis elegans). Length, 18-24".
Small slender snake with brownish upper parts conspicuously marked by 4 rows of blackish or dark brown spots; pale yellow mid-dorsal and side (lateral) stripes; under parts mottled with dusky. Prefers moist areas.

TCH
Grass
Brush
Marsh

11.

TCH
Rocks
Grass
Sage

**11. WESTERN RATTLESNAKE** (Crotalus viridis). Length, 24-28". Stout-bodied snake, with grayish or greenish or brownish upper parts conspicuously marked with a mid-dorsal row of dark brownish blotches bordered laterally by smaller dark spots. Tip of tail with rattle. Dangerously poisonous, feeding on small mammals, ground birds, lizards, etc.

## COMMON AMPHIBIANS

Frogs, toads and salamanders are distinguished by moist slimy non-scaly skins. They frequent water or moist places and usually lay their eggs and spend their larval lives in water. All are harmless and feed mainly on insects and other invertebrates. Figures refer to body lengths.

TCH
Marsh
Rocks
Conif.

1.

**1. LONG-TOED SALAMANDER** (Ambystoma macrodactylum). 2 1/4-3 1/4". A small slender salamander, dark brownish or blackish above with a broad irregular tannish, yellowish, or greenish stripe down center of the back. Sides speckled with white and under parts blackish flecked with small white spots. Under logs, rocks, etc.

2. TIGER SALAMANDER (Ambystoma tigrinum). 3-6". Medium-sized stoutly-built salamander, with black or sooty-brown upper parts and sides heavily spotted with irregular whitish blotches. Under parts somewhat lighter. Some individuals in certain places remain in larval form, though adults. Moist places.

TC
Marsh
Str. Wd.
Conif.

2.

3. PACIFIC GIANT SALAMANDER (Dicamptodon ensatus). 4 1/2-6". Large heavy-bodied salamander. Upper parts grayish, brownish or yellowish with small blotches on the throat and white speckles on sides. In water or under logs or stones nearby. North Idaho & nearby Mont.

TC
Water
Str. Wd.

3.

4. WESTERN TOAD (Bufo boreas). 2 1/2-5". Upper parts grayish, blackish or brownish, mottled with blackish and covered with wart-like protuberances; usually with white stripe down middle of back; under parts mottled grayish. No ridges (cranial crests) between and back of eyes. Usually active at night; occurs in moist open habitats.

TCH
Grass
Str. Wd.
Rocks

5. WOODHOUSE'S TOAD (Bufo woodhousei). 2-4 1/2". Very similar to Western Toad, but with prominent ridges (cranial crests) between and behind eyes. Near water in most of our region except northern Idaho.

T
Grass
Str. Wd.
Marsh
Sage

4.                              6.

6. PACIFIC TREE FROG (Hyla regilla). 1/2-2". Small frog with adhesive discs at tips of toes; upper parts variable, generally greenish or brownish, marked with darker blotches. Black stripe on side of head from nostril to behind eye; white or yellow below. North part of our region.

T
Grass
Str. Wd.
Marsh

7. SWAMP CRICKET-FROG (Pseudacris nigrita). 3/4-1 1/2". Very small frog without adhesive toe pads. Upper parts greenish or brownish with prominent long dark stripes. Eye stripe continuing along body behind fore legs. Moist habitats, particularly meadows, of south part of region.

T
Meadow
Marsh

8.   TAILED FROG (Ascaphus truei).  1 1/2-2". Small frog characterized by vertical eye pupil, no eardrums, and tail-like copulatory organ in ♂. Upper parts reddish or brownish, marked with darker streaks and blotches; prominent eye-stripe; under parts pale yellow. Tadpoles blackish with white fleck on tail; often found clinging by sucker to the under sides of rocks  in streams.  Occurs in or near shallow white water in northern part of region.

CH
Water
Str. Wd.

9.   LEOPARD FROG (Rana pipiens). Smooth-skinned frog with  greenish  or brownish upper parts conspicuously marked with  large   round or oval black spots which are margined by light-colored bands; hind   legs marked by black cross-bars; under parts yellowish or whitish.   Croak of ♂ a low throaty grunting sound.  Usually found in low open areas near water.

T
Meadow
Marsh

10.  SPOTTED FROG (Rana pretiosa).  3-4".  Upper parts roughened with small tubercles; color above light brown, darkening to almost black, with small black spots; pale yellow or whitish stripe from nose to shoulder; dark brownish eye-mask.  Under parts varied: creamy to yellow or red, often spotted and mottled; inner side of hind legs often reddish.

TCH
Water
Marsh
Str. Wd.
Meadow

11.   WESTERN SPADEFOOT TOAD (Scaphiopus hammondi). 1 1/2-2 1/2". Small squatty toad with a greenish or grayish skin roughened by numerous small tubercles and mottled by irregular spots or blotches of brownish or blackish; an irregular band of lighter color extending back from each eye; under parts whitish or grayish.   Characteristic field mark is black rounded sharp-edged   tubercle or "spade" on underside of hind foot.   Nocturnal.  Voice: low-pitched snoring sound; buries itself in sand in dry times.

T
Grass
Water

10.          8.

11.          9.

## SUGGESTED REFERENCES

Abrams, Leroy. 1949-1960. ILLUSTRATED FLORA OF THE PACIFIC STATES, in 4 vols. Stanford.
American Ornithologists' Union. 1957. CHECK LIST OF NORTH AMERICAN BIRDS. 5th ed.    Lord
    Baltimore Press, Baltimore.
Baerg, H. HOW TO KNOW THE WESTERN TREES. 1955. Brown, C. W., Dubuque, Iowa.
Burt, W. H. 1952. A FIELD GUIDE TO THE MAMMALS. Houghton Mifflin, Boston.
Palmer, R. S. 1954. THE MAMMAL GUIDE. Doubleday, New York.
Peterson, R. T. 1961, Revised Edition. A FIELD GUIDE TO WESTERN BIRDS. Houghton Mifflin.
Rydberg, P. A. 1954. FLORA OF THE ROCKY MOUNTAINS AND ADJACENT PLAINS. Hafner.
Salt, W. R. and A. L. Wilk. 1958. THE BIRDS OF ALBERTA. Department of Economic Affairs, Gov-
    ernment of Alberta, Edmonton.
Sanderson, I. T. 1951. HOW TO KNOW THE AMERICAN MAMMALS. Little, Brown, and Co., Boston.
Savage, J. M. 1959. AN ILLUSTRATED KEY TO THE TURTLES, LIZARDS, AND SNAKES OF WES-
    TERN UNITED STATES AND CANADA. Naturegraph Company, Healdsburg, California.
Stebbins, R. C. 1954. AMPHIBIANS AND REPTILES OF WESTERN NORTH AMERICA. McGraw-Hill,
    New York.

## INDEX

(NOTE: In this index individual species are listed by name only if there is just one of the kind in the book
or if the plant or animal belongs to a group, such as the Grasses, which covers several pages. For all
other species, look under group names such as "bats" or "swallows".)